# THE AUTOCAR HANDBOOK

# *The Autocar* Handbook

## COMPLETE GUIDE TO
## THE MODERN CAR

J. R. SINGHAM, Ph.D., B.Sc. (Eng.), A.M.I.Mech.E.

LONDON

ILIFFE & SONS LTD

FIRST PUBLISHED          1906
TWENTY-SECOND EDITION
© ILIFFE & SONS LTD.     1960

Published for " The Autocar " by Iliffe & Sons Ltd
Dorset House, Stamford Street, London, S.E.1
Made and printed in England at the Chapel River Press,
Andover, Hants
Bks 3507

# CONTENTS

# FOREWORD

A HANDBOOK that has been published and in demand in a succession of editions for more than fifty years can fairly claim to be both established and useful. Of course, this latest volume—entirely re-written since the 21st edition appeared in 1953 and now enlarged to 22 chapters—is as different from the very first one as are the cars of today from those of the early 1900's.

Almost everyone has a slight knowledge of a motor car and its main components, although such knowledge is desirable rather than essential for the drivers of modern vehicles. This new edition of *The Autocar* Handbook is similar to its predecessors in that it is not a treatise for the engineer nor a student's textbook, but rather a reference book in which an interested, non-technical motorist may read-up details of cars and their equipment—otherwise the treatment is entirely new.

The material is chatty and easily understood, and there are a great many illustrations, mainly in the form of perspective drawings; actual modern cars are taken as examples for cut-away drawings, each main subject or subject-group being dealt with as an entity, so that there is no need for continuous reading through the book.

Innovations in automobile engineering design have been many in the last decade; new developments which now find a place in production cars—automatic transmissions, overdrives, disc brakes, power-assisted steering and so on—are described in this latest handbook.

The publishers are aware that some motorists have no desire to under-stand their cars, beyond the ability to operate the controls and fill up with petrol, oil and water. In maintaining such an attitude, they are the losers. There is little doubt that the information contained in this book can help owners to get the best out of their cars, to avoid troubles and unnecessary expense, to become more appreciative of good features of design and equipment, and thus to enjoy to the full their journeying on the roads.

Dorset House
March, 1960

THE EDITOR
*The Autocar*

# Chapter I

# A BRIEF SURVEY

THREE-quarters of a century of development have transformed the motor car from a freakish invention enjoyed by a few enthusiasts into a pleasurable means of transport for millions. During this period the design of the car has become steadily more elaborate whilst the effort required to drive and maintain it has steadily decreased. One switches on the ignition (Fig. 1.1) and starts the engine by pressing a

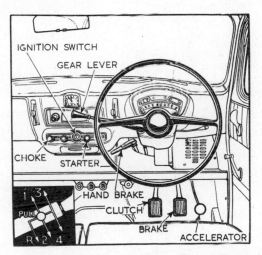

*Fig. 1.1. Driving controls of a modern car. The inset diagram shows a typical arrangement for the gear lever positions (viewed from the left)*

button, pulling a knob, or giving a further turn to the ignition key. If the engine is cold, it will probably be necessary to " richen the mixture " by pulling out the " choke ", but this too may be done automatically. Next, one puts the engine " in gear " by depressing the clutch pedal with the left foot and pushing the gear lever from " neutral " into " first ". Finally one releases the hand brake and presses the accelerator pedal gently with the right foot whilst gradually releasing the clutch pedal—and away one goes. Simple though this procedure may be, the present trend is towards even greater simplicity of control. On many cars, the clutch pedal has disappeared; one simply moves the gear lever in order to change gear. On more expensive models, one can forget about gear changing entirely, since it is carried out quite automatically.

But it is one thing to be able to drive a car and quite another to understand it. The aim of this book is to explain clearly and simply just how the modern motor car works and to describe its main features. It would not be possible in a book of this size to describe all the numerous design variations to be found on modern cars, even if this were considered desirable. Generally speaking it has been thought preferable to concentrate the explanation on a typical example rather than lose sight of the essential principles in a mass of detail. Sometimes certain minor details of a particular design have been omitted in order to make the explanation clearer.

The aim of the present chapter is to make a brief survey of the whole car and to provide some sort of guide to the whole book. For this purpose the chapter is divided into the following sections:

> The Engine
> The Transmission
> The Body and Chassis
> Electrical and other equipment.

Each section consists of a short discussion of that particular aspect of the motor car followed by a table showing which chapters of this book deal with that aspect.

### The Engine

The use of steam engines on the railways was the first major application of mechanical power to surface transport. Later on, a number of

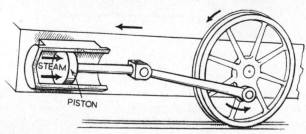

*Fig.* 1.2. *Reciprocating motion is used both in the steam locomotive and in the petrol engine of a motor car. The petrol engine uses hot gases in place of steam and it is coupled to the wheels through a more elaborate transmission*

successful steam-driven cars was developed. The steam engine, however, suffers from certain disadvantages (discussed in Chapter 15) which prevented steam cars from achieving a success comparable to that of railway steam engines.

The engines used on the overwhelming majority of motor cars today are petrol engines whose ancestry can be traced back to the fast-running engine invented by Daimler in the 1880's. The steam engine and the petrol engine are both reciprocating engines. In the steam engine (Fig. 1.2) the piston is forced outwards by the pressure of steam which is generated in a boiler by the *external* combustion of coal or other fuel. In the petrol engine, however, the pressure on the piston is developed by the combustion of a mixture of petrol and air *inside* the cylinder.

### Table. I.   The Engine

| Chapter No. | Title | Aspects Discussed |
|---|---|---|
| 2 | Fundamentals of the Petrol Engine | How a simple petrol engine works; mixture strength; horse-power, torque and m.e.p. |
| 3 | The Popular Overhead Valve Engine | Mechanical design of a typical modern overhead valve engine |
| 4 | Engine Design Features | Variations in engine design; combustion chamber features; cylinder arrangements; firing order; crankshaft design; valve timing; the two-stroke |
| 5 | Producing the Mixture | The carburettor; petrol injection; super-charging; air filtration and silencing |
| 6 | Producing the Spark | Principles of spark ignition; ignition equipment |
| 7 | The Petrol Supply | The petrol system; petrol and other fuels; compression ratio and " pinking "; octane rating |
| 8 | Engine Lubrication | Need for lubrication; the lubrication system; classification of oils |
| 9 | Engine Cooling | Air and water cooling; the radiator, fan and water cooling system |
| 15 | Alternatives to the Petrol Engine | The Diesel engine; the gas turbine; the free piston engine; the gas engine; the electric car; the steam car; the atomic car |

Hence the term " internal combustion engine ". This principle results in an engine which is light, powerful, inexpensive, economical and easy to start.

Table 1 lists the chapters which deal mainly with the engine and shows the particular aspects dealt with.

## The Transmission

The transmission of a car is the mechanical system through which the engine power is transmitted to the road wheels. On a railway steam locomotive, the transmission is extremely simple, power being transmitted directly from engine to wheel through the connecting rod (Fig. 1.2). On a motor car, however, the transmission is more elaborate. The connecting rods drive a crankshaft which is part of the engine and the drive is then transmitted through the clutch and gear box, usually to the back axle via a long propelling shaft. In the days of the " crash " gear box, considerable skill was required in making a speedy and silent gear change, but the introduction of synchromesh gears greatly simplified the operation. The process has been carried further by the development of automatic clutches and gear boxes which has led to " two-pedal " and fully automatic control on many cars.

Table 2 lists the chapters dealing with the transmission and briefly indicates the contents of each.

## The Body and Chassis

There are two principal ways of building a motor car. The first, which was practically universal until a few years ago, is to build the car in two sections, namely, the chassis and the body. With this method, the chassis can be likened to a mechanically propelled trolley carrying an independently built body. The second way, which has now been widely adopted, particularly in Europe, is to make the chassis frame integral with the body and to install the engine and transmission in this body-chassis unit.

The chapters listed in Table 3 refer to both combined and separate bodies and chassis.

## Electrical and other Equipment

An efficient electricity supply system is an essential part of the modern car, the heart of the system being a battery kept charged automatically by an engine-driven dynamo. Electricity is required firstly for producing the spark which ignites the mixture of petrol and air in the engine cylinder and secondly for operating the lights and numerous accessories. To produce the ignition spark, a special high voltage electrical supply

4

Table 2.  The Transmission

| Chapter No. | Title | Aspects Discussed |
|---|---|---|
| 10 | The Clutch | Need for clutch; mechanical construction |
| 11 | Making Use of the Engine | Need for gearing; gear boxes; overdrive |
| 12 | The Drive to the Road Wheels | The propeller shaft; crown wheel and pinion; rear axle and differential; rear engines; front wheel drive |
| 13 | Two-Pedal Control | Automatic clutch operation; vacuum-operated clutch; magnetic clutch; hydraulic clutch operation |
| 14 | Automatic Transmission | The fluid coupling; fluid torque converter; epicyclic gearing; automatic control |

Table 3.  The Body and Chassis

| Chapter No. | Title | Aspects Discussed |
|---|---|---|
| 16 | Wheels, Tyres and Brakes | Disc and wire wheels; tubed and tubeless tyres; the braking problem; drum brakes; hydraulic operation; disc brakes; vacuum servo-assisted brakes |
| 17 | Suspension, Springs and Shock Absorbers | Leaf spring suspension; independent front wheel suspension; shock absorbers; rear suspension |
| 18 | Steering | The steering linkage; steering gear; principles of steering; power-assisted steering |
| 19 | The Body Structure | The trend in design; chassis-less construction; streamlining and wind resistance; body materials |
| 20 | Body Details | Paintwork; corrosion prevention; chromium plating; windscreens and windows; doors and roofs; seating and decoration |

is required but the lights and other electrical equipment operate at battery voltage. Table 4 shows the chapters dealing with the ignition and electrical systems and with electrical and non-electrical equipment.

**Table 4. Electrical and other Equipment**

| Chapter No. | Title | Aspects Discussed |
|---|---|---|
| 6 | Producing the Spark | Principles of spark ignition; ignition equipment |
| 21 | The Electrical System | The battery; the dynamo and charging system; the starter; lighting; the wiring system |
| 22 | Equipment and Accessories | Mirrors; windscreen wipers and washers; direction indicators; the horn; instruments; heaters; radiator blinds; radio; gadgets |

# Chapter 2

# FUNDAMENTALS OF THE PETROL ENGINE

IF we fill a metal box with a mixture of compressed air and petrol vapour and fire the mixture by means of an electric spark, the pressure in the container is greatly increased. A weak container, such as a petrol can, would certainly burst. Evidently then a mixture of petrol and air can be a source of great energy; the petrol engine is simply a device for releasing this energy in an orderly manner and converting it into as much useful work as possible.

### How the Petrol Engine Works

Engines used for transport nearly always use more than one cylinder but the principle of operation is the same as for the single-cylinder, four-stroke engine shown in Fig. 2.1. The illustration shows a vertical *cylinder* containing a sliding *piston* which is linked to a *crankshaft* by a *connecting rod*. When the piston moves up and down the cylinder the crankshaft is made to turn, rather as an up and down motion from the knee causes the chain wheel of a bicycle to turn. At the top end of the cylinder there are two openings or *ports* which can be opened or closed by the inlet and exhaust *valves*. The piston moves up and down twice in a complete cycle of operation, which corresponds to two revolutions of the crankshaft. The *camshaft*, which is driven from the crankshaft, has two *cams* which act on the inlet and exhaust valves through a simple mechanism, causing them to open and close at the required moments.

Fig. 2.1 shows the piston near the top of the cylinder with the exhaust valve closed and the inlet valve open. If the crankshaft is turned by hand, the piston descends and a charge of air is drawn into the cylinder. The amount of air drawn in may be large or small depending on the opening of the throttle valve in the carburettor. As the air passes through the carburettor, it causes a suction around the petrol jet so that petrol is swept into the cylinder with the incoming air. This *induction* or *suction* stroke is shown in simplified form in stage (a) of Fig. 2.2. As the crankshaft continues to turn, the piston reaches the bottom of its stroke and then starts to rise. By this time, rotation of the inlet cam has caused the inlet valve to close and the mixture gets compressed into the top of the cylinder, *compression* stroke, stage (b). Whilst very little effort was required to turn the crankshaft during the first or induction stroke, during the compression stroke the pressure of the mixture increases and resists the movement of the piston so that a considerable effort is required. The work done on the mixture during this stroke causes its temperature to rise, and any droplets of petrol suspended in the air are completely vaporized. Towards the end of the compression stroke, a spark passes across the points of the sparking plug and a flame is initiated which spreads rapidly throughout the mixture and produces a sharp rise of pressure. The force due to the pressure of the hot gases acting on the piston during the *expansion* stroke, stage (c),

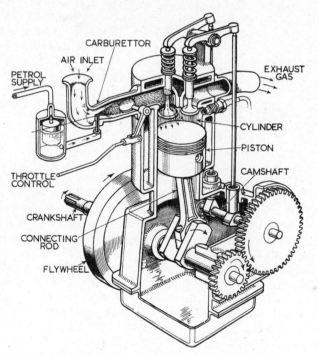

Fig. 2.1. *A simple petrol engine in single-cylinder form. The overhead valves are driven through the gears on the right*

is transmitted to the crankshaft and flywheel—the engine has " fired " and will now operate under its own power. Towards the end of the expansion stroke, the exhaust cam causes the exhaust valve to open and the remaining pressure of the gases is dissipated in a surge into the exhaust pipe. As the piston rises during the fourth and final stroke, the burnt gases left in the cylinder are forced out through the exhaust port, *exhaust* stroke, stage (d). At the end of the exhaust stroke, the exhaust valve closes and the inlet valve opens ready for the next cycle.

Since a cycle consists of four complete strokes, the engine is said to operate on the *four-stroke cycle* and the engine is referred to as a *four-stroke*

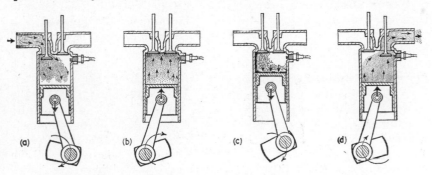

Fig. 2.2.  Most petrol engines operate on a cycle consisting of four main processes, each of which corresponds to an upward or downward movement of the piston

| (*a*) Induction or suction stroke: inlet valve open; petrol/air mixture enters cylinder as piston descends. Inlet valve closes at end of stroke | (*b*) Compression stroke: both valves closed; piston rises so compressing petrol/air mixture. Spark occurs near end of stroke causing rapid combustion of mixture | (*c*) Expansion stroke: gases now at high pressure and temperature expand forcing pistons downwards; power is transmitted to crankshaft. Exhaust valve opens at end of stroke | (*d*) Exhaust stroke: exhaust valve opens; piston rises so expelling burnt gases from cylinder. At end of stroke, exhaust valve closes and inlet opens |

*engine.* A petrol engine can also be made to operate on a cycle consisting of only two complete strokes, but the four-stroke cycle is much more common. The *two-stroke engine* is dealt with in Chapter 4.

An engine in which combustion takes place inside a cylinder is known as an *internal combustion engine*—this description distinguishes it from engines such as the steam engine where combustion of the fuel takes place outside the engine in the boiler. The petrol engine is the most familiar type of internal combustion (I.C.) engine, but the *diesel engine*, dealt with in Chapter 15, also belongs to this class. The petrol engine, the diesel engine and the steam engine all use a piston and crankshaft mechanism and are therefore described as *reciprocating engines*. This description distinguishes them from the *gas turbine* (dealt with in Chapter 15) in which the motion is purely rotary.

Work is transmitted by the piston to the crankshaft in a series of pulses since only every fourth stroke is a firing stroke. If the engine is driving a motor car then a continuous turning force or torque is required

9

from the crankshaft. Furthermore, considerable work is done by the crankshaft on the mixture during the compression stroke and a certain amount of work has to be done during the induction and exhaust strokes as well. To meet these requirements, a heavy *flywheel* is mounted on the crankshaft. During the expansion stroke, the work not required for propelling the car goes into speeding up the flywheel. During the next three strokes the flywheel returns this energy and slows down to its original speed. As the flywheel is large and heavy compared with the amount of energy to be stored, the fluctuation of speed is fairly small and the drive is sufficiently smooth and continuous for most purposes.

### Amounts of Petrol and Air in a " Correct " Mixture

In discussing the petrol engine we often speak of a " chemically correct " petrol-air mixture, by which we usually mean a mixture containing the maximum amount of petrol that can be burnt completely with the oxygen available in the air. If there is too little petrol, some of the oxygen will be left over; if there is too much, the petrol will not be burnt completely. Petrol consists of carbon and hydrogen joined together chemically. If we take 100 lb of petrol (about 14 gallons) and split it up into its chemical components we shall find that it contains about 86 lb of carbon and 14 lb of hydrogen. Other elements may be present in small quantities but, for our present purposes, these are negligible. For complete combustion of the petrol, a quantity of air must be supplied containing sufficient oxygen for combustion of both the carbon and the hydrogen. We know from experiment that 1 lb carbon requires 2·67 lb of oxygen for its complete combustion into 3·67 lb of carbon dioxide, whilst 1 lb of hydrogen will combine with 8 lb of oxygen to form 9 lb of water vapour. From these figures we can calculate the oxygen required for combustion of 100 lb of petrol:

Oxygen to combine with 86 lb carbon, $86 \times 2\cdot67 = 230$ lb

,, ,, ,, ,, 14 lb hydrogen, $14 \times 8 = 112$ lb

Total oxygen required $= 342$ lb

Now for every 1 lb of oxygen required, we must have 4·35 lb of air since the amount of oxygen in the air is only about 23 per cent. So to get 342 lb of oxygen we must have $4\cdot35 \times 342$ lb of air, that is, 1,490 lb. Thus 100 lb of petrol require 1,490 lb of air for complete combustion, that is 14·9 lb of air to 1 lb of petrol.

This air requirement means that when an engine consumes a gallon of petrol, it uses the amount of air contained in a room 14 ft long, 10 ft wide and 10 ft high. Without this air, the engine cannot work, a difficulty to be overcome before we can spend our motoring holidays on

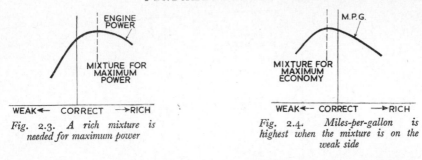

*Fig. 2.3. A rich mixture is needed for maximum power*

*Fig. 2.4. Miles-per-gallon is highest when the mixture is on the weak side*

Mars or the Moon. Even on earth, the power available in mountainous regions is appreciably reduced owing to the rarefied atmosphere.

A *weak* or *lean* mixture is one containing less than the correct amount of petrol whilst a *rich* mixture is one containing more petrol than can be burnt with the oxygen available. For a petrol engine to run satisfactorily the mixture must be more or less correct. Fig. 2.3 shows how the power delivered by an engine is found to vary with mixture strength. For maximum power we require a mixture that is slightly rich. If the mixture is too weak or much too rich then the engine power falls away rapidly. Fig. 2.4 shows the variation of miles to the gallon (m.p.g.) with mixture strength from which we see that maximum economy calls for a slightly weak mixture. If the mixture is too rich or too weak, the m.p.g. falls and we lose in economy. The carburettor is responsible for regulating mixture strength to the required value and the subject is dealt with further in Chapter 5 in connection with carburettors.

The main constituents in the exhaust gas from a petrol engine are carbon dioxide, water vapour and nitrogen. Carbon dioxide, which is also formed when animals breathe, is already present in the atmosphere and is not poisonous. However, when carbon burns incompletely, *carbon monoxide* is formed and this is extremely dangerous since it is poisonous but has very little smell. Traces of the gas are always present in the exhaust of a motor car and it is for this reason that the engine should never be run in a closed garage. The water vapour in the exhaust is usually invisible, but on a cold day, soon after the engine has been started, vapour condenses in a cloud behind the exhaust pipe; some of the vapour condenses into water in the pipe itself and can be seen dripping from the exhaust. Nitrogen, of course, is the main constituent of the atmosphere, and it passes through the engine without taking any active part in combustion.

### Where the Energy Goes

Measurements show that when 1 lb of petrol is burnt (rather less than a pint) about 19,000 British Thermal Units (B.t.u.) of heat are

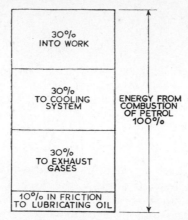

Fig. 2.5. *The shaft output of a petrol engine only amounts to about 30 per cent of the heating value of the petrol*

made available. The B.t.u. is the unit of heat and is the amount of heat required to raise the temperature of 1 lb of water ($\frac{4}{5}$ pint) by 1°F. If we were to attach a paddle wheel to the output shaft of a petrol engine so that all the work output was dissipated in raising the temperature of a tank of water, we could measure the heat equivalent of the work output. We should find that only about one third of the heating value of the petrol appeared as work output. The exact pro-

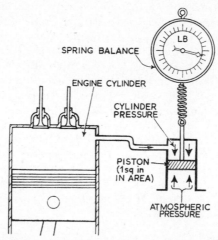

Fig. 2.6. *The diagram shows how the pressure in an engine might be measured. If the spring balance reading was 50 lb, the pressure in the engine cylinder would be 50 lb/in.[2]*

portion would depend on the design of the engine, the proportion being greatest for engines of high compression ratio, but the proportion would not reach a half even for the most modern engine. The explanation of this unfortunate state of affairs is not the incompetence of engine designers but the scientific impossibility of turning a given amount of heat into the equivalent amount of work. Even a perfectly designed petrol engine of 10 to 1 compression ratio could only convert 60 per cent of the petrol's available energy into work, whilst the remainder would be carried away in the exhaust gases. In any practical engine there is a further inevitable source of loss. Unless the engine cylinder were kept reasonably cool, it would be impossible to keep the piston lubricated so that it slid smoothly in the cylinder; also the life of the valves would be very short. Consequently all practical engines must have some form of cooling—either a circulation of cooling water through the engine to a radiator or a supply of cooling air blown over the outside of the engine. The amount of heat lost in this way is of the same order as the amount of energy turned into useful work, as can be seen from Fig. 2.5. The subject of engine cooling is dealt with further in Chapter 9.

### Work Done on the Piston by the Cylinder Gases

We have said that the pressure of the gases in the cylinder acts on the piston and causes power to be transmitted to the engine crankshaft. In order to understand the process, we must be clear about the meaning of the term " pressure of the gases ". All gases exert a force on any surface with which they are in contact. If the force is measured in pounds then the force acting on one square inch of surface is called the *pressure* of the gases and is measured in pounds per square inch (lb/in.$^2$). The pressure of the atmosphere, for instance, is about 14·7 lb/in.$^2$ at sea level (this is the same as the pressure due to a column of mercury 29·9 in. high—the reading given by a barometer). When an engine is at rest the pressure in the cylinder due to the atmosphere is 14·7 lb/in.$^2$, but the piston does not, of course, move, since the atmospheric pressure also acts on the opposite side of the piston. The important thing to know about the cylinder pressure is not the true pressure as defined above (usually called the " absolute " pressure) but the excess of the true pressure over the atmospheric pressure. This value is called the *gauge* pressure and a simple method of measuring it is illustrated in Fig. 2.6. As the pressure in an engine fluctuates rapidly, it would be impossible to read the dial without some additional equipment—one possibility would be to photograph the dial with a high-speed ciné camera, and project the film in slow motion. The method shown, though simple in principle, would be cumbersome in practice, and measurements of cylinder pressure in modern engines usually make use of elaborate electronic equipment. The instrument used for measuring cylinder pressure is referred to as an indicator.

The type of record that can be obtained is shown in Fig. 2.7, from which the pressure at any point in the cycle can be seen. During the suction stroke the piston moves from left to right and the pressure falls slightly below atmospheric pressure; the resulting pressure difference causes air from the atmosphere to flow into the cylinder. The pressure rises throughout the compression stroke, and there is a further sharp rise

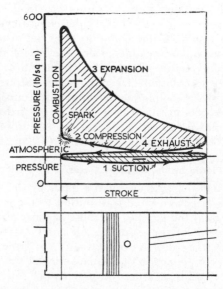

*Fig. 2.7. The variation of cylinder pressure during each of the four strokes can be represented on a pressure-stroke diagram*

when combustion takes place following the spark at the end of this stroke. During the expansion stroke, the pressure falls gradually; at the end of the stroke the exhaust valve opens and there is a more sudden drop in pressure as the gases escape into the atmosphere. The exhaust stroke follows, during which the piston forces the remaining exhaust gases from the cylinder, the pressure being slightly above the atmospheric pressure. The force acting on the piston is found by multiplying the cylinder gauge pressure by the piston area, e.g. if the cylinder pressure at any instant is 400 lb/in.$^2$, and the piston is 6 in.$^2$, the net force on the piston is 2,400 lb.

We are interested at present in finding out the work done by the gases on the piston. Work is a scientific term as well as an everyday expression, and is something that can be exactly measured. The engineer's unit of work is the foot-pound, which is the work done when a force of one pound is exerted over a distance of one foot. If, for example, a trunk weighing 100 lb is lifted upstairs through a vertical distance of 9 ft the work done is 900 ft-lb, that is work is (force) × (distance). Similarly, in the previous example, if the piston moves a distance of $\frac{1}{10}$ ft, say, whilst the pressure remains constant, the work done is 2,400 × $\frac{1}{10}$ = 240 ft-lb. In fact, as we have seen, the pressure varies as the piston moves, so we have to use an average cylinder pressure in order to find the total work done on the piston. If we divide the net positive area of the pressure diagram by the stroke, we get a height corresponding to the *mean effective pressure*—usually somewhere about 100 lb/in². This means that the work done during the whole cycle is equivalent to a steady pressure during expansion of 100 lb/in². The mean effective pressure (m.e.p.) is a very useful quantity since it tells us how effective the gases are, quite apart from the size of the engine or the speed at which it runs. It is usually described as the *indicated* mean effective pressure since it is measured using a pressure indicator as described earlier. (*Brake mean effective pressure* is mentioned at the end of the chapter.) If the piston area is 6 in.² and the m.e.p. is 100 lb/in.², then the effective force during expansion will be 100 × 6 = 600 lb; if the piston stroke is 3 in., i.e. $\frac{3}{12}$ ft, the work done on the piston is 600 × $\frac{3}{12}$ = 150 ft-lb per cycle. In the next section we shall see how this is related to the horse-power.

### The Horse-power of an Engine

In the early days of the motor car it was possible to get a rough estimate of the maximum horse-power of an engine from the R.A.C. formula:

$$\text{Horse-power} = \frac{(\text{cylinder diameter in inches})^2 \times (\text{number of cylinders})}{2 \cdot 5}$$

The formula takes no account of engine stroke, engine speed, nor the mean effective pressure, all of which affect the horse-power, but for the speeds, pressures and stroke/bore ratios common at the time (the bore is the cylinder diameter) the formula was reasonably accurate, and was used for taxation and insurance purposes. Since then, engine speeds and pressures have greatly increased, and the true horse-power of an engine is often four times as great as its R.A.C. rating. Apart from its inaccuracy, the formula eventually became an artificial factor influencing the designer's choice of cylinder stroke/bore ratio and retarded the design of British engines for a number of years—the designer used a small bore to keep the rated horse-power low, and used a long stroke in order to increase the actual power. The formula was abandoned for taxation purposes in 1947 and is no longer of any value. Nevertheless, the R.A.C. rating served a useful purpose—it was convenient to be able to describe a car as " a sixteen horse " or an Austin 7. The question

15

therefore arises of what description to use in its place. The best simple description is probably the cylinder capacity or " swept volume "—that is (piston area) × (piston stroke) × (number of cylinders). The capacity is usually expressed in cubic centimetres (c.c.) or in litres, a litre being 1,000 c.c. We then discover from experience that 850 c.c. represents a small car like the Austin 7, whilst $3\frac{1}{2}$ litres represents something fairly powerful like the Jaguar. But if we want to know the real power of the car we must ask—what is the *brake horse-power* (b.h.p.)?

The engineer measures the power of an engine, that is the rate at which it does work, in terms of horse-power. A horse-power is roughly equal to the power of a heavy cart horse, but the engineer defines a horse-power precisely as a rate of work equal to 33,000 foot-pounds per minute. The horse in Fig. 2.8 is exerting a force of 100 lb and is moving at a rate of 330 ft/min—it is doing work at a rate of 100 × 330 = 33,000 ft-lb/min, and is therefore developing 1 horse-power. In the previous section we saw that an engine with a piston area of 6 in.$^2$ and a stroke of 3 in. produced 150 ft-lb of work per cycle for a mean effective pressure of 100 lb/in$^2$. To find the horse-power we need to know the rotational speed of the engine. Let us suppose that the engine is running at 2,000 revolutions per minute (2,000 r.p.m.). A complete cycle of four strokes occupies two revolutions of the crankshaft, so there will be 1,000 cycles per minute. The power output is therefore 1,000 × 150 = 150,000 ft-lb per minute and the horse-power is $\dfrac{150,000}{33,000} = 4 \cdot 55$. If the engine has several cylinders we must multiply this figure by the number of cylinders —a four-cylinder engine would therefore develop 4 × 4·55 = 18·2 h.p.

The word brake in the expression brake-horse-power conveys the fact that we are dealing with the power developed at the engine output shaft (owing to friction, this is somewhat less than the power transferred to the piston by the gases). The machine used for measuring the power of an engine on the test-bed acts as a brake on the engine by absorbing its power, and the machines themselves are often referred to as brakes.

In this chapter the discussion has been confined to four-stroke engines. Similar calculations could be made for the two-stroke engine, bearing in mind the fact that the two-stroke engine fires once for every revolution of the crankshaft. The two-stroke engine is discussed in Chapter 4.

### Torque: The Turning Effort of the Engine Crankshaft

The forces exerted by the cylinder gases on the piston are transmitted through the connecting rod to the crankshaft, and the presence of the flywheel ensures a steady turning effort from the engine. This turning effort is called the *torque* of the engine, and it is a very important quantity, since it is the torque that determines the acceleration of a car or the gradient that can be tackled. It can be understood by considering the action of an ordinary capstan (see Fig. 2.9). To raise the load, the man must apply a turning effort equal to the resisting effort of the load. Experience shows that the greater his distance from the centre of the capstan, the smaller the force that he needs to exert. If we measure the force required at various radii, we find that for a given load on the

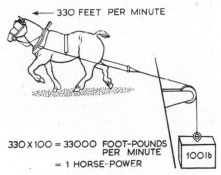

Fig. 2.8.   *A horse-power is equal to 33,000 foot-pounds per minute*

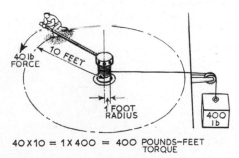

Fig. 2.9.   *A torque is equivalent to a force acting at a certain radius*

capstan, the quantity (force) × (radius) is constant. Further, it is equal to the quantity (force of load on capstan rope) × (radius of capstan). The quantity (force) × (radius) is the torque—if the capstan radius is 1 ft and the load is 400 lb, the resisting torque is 400 lb-ft. If the man works at a radius of 10 ft he will have to exert a force of 40 lb in order to produce the same torque, and so overcome the resistance. We should notice that the torque does not tell us the rate at which the man is doing work—he may be walking fast or very slowly, but the torque remains the same.

In the same way the torque of an engine tells us the turning resistance that can be overcome at the output shaft—this is the information we require when calculating the gradient that a car can ascend. The power output can be calculated from the torque, if we know the rotational speed of the shaft. Returning to the capstan example, for every complete turn of the capstan the man walks a distance of $2\pi \times$ (radius). (The circumference of a circle is equal to its radius multiplied by $2\pi$, commonly known as $2\pi r$; $\pi$ is a number approximately equal to $\frac{22}{7}$.) If he is making a certain number of revolutions in one minute, then he is walking at a rate of $2\pi r \times$ (r.p.m.) ft/min. His rate of work is the distance walked per minute multiplied by the force exerted, i.e. rate of work $= 2\pi r \times$ (r.p.m.) $\times$ (force) ft-lb/min. We have seen that (force) $\times$ (radius) is (torque), so we can rewrite the rate of work as $2\pi \times$ (r.p.m.) $\times$ (torque). If we divide by 33,000 we shall have the power output in h.p. (since 1 h.p. $= 33,000$ ft-lb/min). So we arrive at the formula,

$$\text{Horse-power} = \frac{2\pi \times \text{(r.p.m.)} \times \text{(torque)}}{33,000}$$

It is much easier to measure the power of an engine by using this formula than to calculate it from measurements of cylinder pressure in the manner described earlier. The engineer simply measures the torque by attaching a brake to the output shaft, and measures the r.p.m. using a " rev " counter. He can then find the power from this formula in a matter of seconds, using his slide-rule. If the torque is 100 lb-ft at 2,000 r.p.m., the horse-power is found thus:

$$\text{B.h.p.} = \frac{2 \times \frac{22}{7} \times 2,000 \times 100}{33,000} = 38 \text{ h.p.}$$

If the engine is driving its auxiliaries when the brake power is measured (i.e. fan, dynamo, etc.) the power measured is the *net* b.h.p. Often, engines are tested without auxiliaries and the power measured is referred to as the *gross* b.h.p. The difference between the two is often considerable and it is always desirable to make it clear which figure is being quoted.

In the last section, we saw how the power could be calculated from the indicated mean effective pressure (i.m.e.p.). This indicated power is always more than the brake power owing to frictional losses in the piston and crankshaft mechanism. Often, the engineer works in the other direction and calculates the mean effective pressure from either the net or the gross b.h.p.; this gives a quantity known as the *brake* mean effective pressure (net or gross). The b.m.e.p. is a very useful basis of comparison for engines, since it is not directly affected by engine size and speed.

# Chapter 3

# THE POPULAR OVERHEAD VALVE ENGINE

MOST of the popular British makes of car manufactured today are fitted with an engine of the type described in this chapter. Whilst the details of construction may vary from one make to another, these engines conform to the following general description:

1. The engine is mounted at the front of the vehicle and has four or six cylinders arranged vertically in a line from front to rear.
2. The cylinders are water-cooled and the cooling water is made to circulate through the engine and radiator by means of a small water pump incorporated in the engine.
3. The engine operates on the four-stroke cycle described in the last chapter.
4. The valves are mounted overhead in the cylinder head and are operated by a single camshaft mounted in the cylinder block.

Side-valve engines are almost extinct so far as current motor-car engines are concerned; discussion of this type is deferred until Chapter 4. In the U.S.A., V-8 engines are very popular though six-cylinder engines are preferred for those cars intended to give economy instead of power. The V-8 engine has two banks of four cylinders arranged to form a V-shape, but in respect of its water-cooling and overhead valves the American engine has much in common with the popular British type of engine described in this chapter. On the Continent, air-cooled engines and two-stroke engines are often used but their application is limited to the smaller cars. The air-cooled engine is mentioned in Chapter 9 whilst the two-stroke engine is dealt with in Chapter 4.

### Advantages of a Multi-cylinder Engine

The engine described in the last chapter had only one cylinder. All the power transmitted to the crankshaft was due to the pressure of the hot gases acting on a single piston. Such an engine embodies all the essential features of a petrol engine and indeed many early motor cars had single-cylinder engines. But an engine with several cylinders has certain advantages which make it essential nowadays except for motor

cycles and midget economy cars.  One important advantage is less noise
—as a single-cylinder engine only fires once for every two turns of the
crankshaft, the pressure in the exhaust pipe rises and falls rapidly when
the exhaust valve opens.   In a four-cylinder engine of the same power,
each cylinder is very much smaller and there are four small pulses instead
of a large single pulse.   The pressure fluctuation in the exhaust pipe
is very much less and the engine is more easily silenced.

Another advantage of the multi-cylinder engine is smoothness of
running.   The crankshaft receives several small impulses instead of a
large single impulse and the torque is therefore much steadier.   As a
result, a smaller flywheel can be used, the engine runs more smoothly

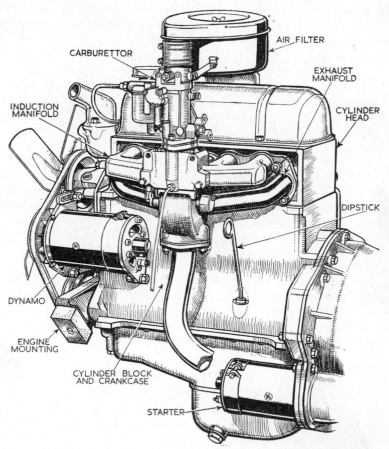

*Fig. 3.1.   Side view of a typical four-cylinder, overhead valve engine*

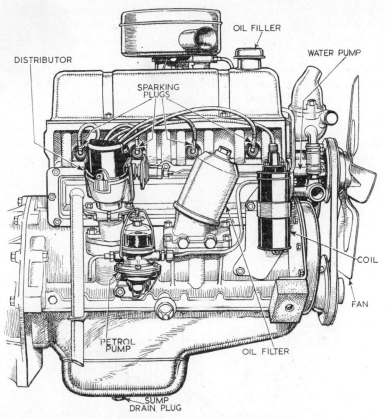

OIL FILLER

DISTRIBUTOR

WATER PUMP

SPARKING
PLUGS

COIL

FAN

PETROL
PUMP

OIL FILTER

SUMP
DRAIN PLUG

*Fig. 3.2. Opposite side of engine shown in Fig. 3.1. The tubes alongside the sparking plugs enclose the push-rods for the overhead valves*

and the wear on the transmission and tyres is considerably less. The forces arising from the reciprocating motion itself also add to the noise and vibration in a single-cylinder engine, whereas in a multi-cylinder engine it is possible to arrange for the forces in the various cylinders to cancel each other out to a considerable extent. The question of number and arrangement of cylinders is discussed further in Chapter 4.

**A Glance under the Bonnet**

The external appearance of a typical four-cylinder engine is illustrated in Figs. 3.1 and 3.2, which show opposite sides of the same engine. In Fig. 3.3, part of the engine has been cut away to reveal the moving parts and the inner construction. The main structural component is a large iron casting which forms the cylinder block and crankcase. This monobloc type of construction as it is called eliminates the joint between the crankcase and cylinder block thereby reducing the cost of machining and assembling the engine. Moreover, a single casting can be made extremely rigid and the permanent alignment of the crankshaft with the cylinders is assured. The top of the block is closed by the cylinder head casting which is secured by studs fixed in the cylinder block as shown in Fig. 3.4. These studs are made of tough steel in order to withstand the full force of the explosion which amounts to about 2 tons per cylinder in an engine of three inch cylinder bore. In order to ensure a joint that is both air- and water-tight, a gasket made of soft copper-sheathed asbestos or corrugated steel is inserted between the faces.

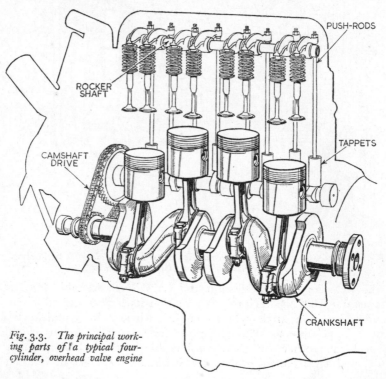

PUSH-RODS

ROCKER SHAFT

CAMSHAFT DRIVE

TAPPETS

CRANKSHAFT

*Fig. 3.3. The principal working parts of a typical four-cylinder, overhead valve engine*

The cylinder head nuts must be equally tightened otherwise there is a danger of leakage or of overstraining some of the studs. On some engines the cylinder head is held down by bolts rather than by separate studs and nuts, the bolts being screwed into the cylinder head.

The valves and valve-operating gear in the cylinder head are protected from dirt by a valve cover which serves also to prevent the escape of fumes and lubricating oil. The valve cover is often connected to the engine air inlet by a small pipe so that fumes are automatically drawn into the engine. Lubricating oil is added to the engine when required through the filler cap in the valve cover. Drain passages are provided in the cylinder head and block so that the oil can collect in the sump beneath the crankcase. The sump is a light steel pressing, bolted to

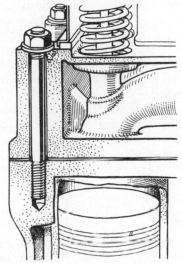

*Fig. 3.4. The cylinder head is usually clamped to the cylinder block by means of studs and nuts, the studs being tightly screwed into the block during manufacture*

a flange on the crankcase; it is provided with a drain plug so that the oil can be removed when dirty. The level of the oil in the sump can be ascertained by means of the dipstick.

The air inlet and exhaust gas manifolds are bolted to one side of the cylinder head, in this case, the left-hand side as seen by the driver. The carburettor is attached to the air inlet manifold and draws air from the combined air filter and silencer immediately above it. The exhaust pipe, which carries the exhaust gases to the rear of the car, is bolted to a flange on the exhaust manifold.

The crankshaft extends from the front of the engine to the rear and carries a flywheel at the rear end from which the drive to the rear wheels is taken. The front end of the crankshaft carries a pulley which drives both the fan pulley and the dynamo pulley through a rubber belt having a vee-shaped cross-section. The fan has two or four blades and draws cooling air through the radiator which is situated immediately in front of it. The cooling water circulating pump is housed in the cylinder block behind the fan and is driven by the same pulley. The water pump draws water from the bottom of the radiator through a rubber hose, forces it through the cylinder block and cylinder head and then through another rubber hose to the top of the radiator, so completing the circuit. A fuller account of the cooling system, including a description of the thermostat, will be given in Chapter 9. The electric starter motor, which is similar in appearance to the dynamo, is bolted to a plate at the rear of the engine, on the left-hand side in this case. Some designers, however, prefer the starter and dynamo to be mounted on the other side away from the hot exhaust manifold. To guard against the possibility of failure of either the battery or the electric starter, it is usual for the front of the crankshaft to be equipped with small dog-teeth so that a starting handle can be used. However, the reliability of modern electrical equipment and the need for the utmost economy in manufacture is such that certain modern cars are without this elementary safeguard.

By placing the inlet and exhaust manifolds on the same side of the cylinder head, the other side is left free for the sparking plugs which screw into the cylinder head. The spark is produced by the action of the coil and distributor and it is natural for these two components to be located on the sparking-plug side of the engine. As its name suggests, the distributor is required to distribute the sparks to the four plugs in the correct sequence and at the correct instant and it must therefore be mechanically driven by the engine. However, each cylinder only requires a spark every two turns of the crankshaft, so the drive is taken from the camshaft which runs at half crankshaft speed. The operation of the ignition system is discussed fully in Chapter 6.

Two other components which are readily spotted during a glance under the bonnet are the petrol pump and the oil filter. As the carburettor is above the level of the petrol in the tank, a small low-pressure pump is required to raise the petrol to this level. On the engine shown in Fig. 3.2 the pump is mechanically driven by an eccentric on the camshaft (Chapter 7 deals with both electric and mechanical petrol pumps). A hand-priming lever is often provided for use when the engine has been standing idle for a long period. The function of the oil filter is of course to remove dirt from the lubricating oil and so protect the bearings and cylinder bores from excessive wear. The oil is circulated by a small pump located in the sump; frequently the pump and distributor have a common drive. Lubrication is discussed in Chapter 8.

### The Mechanical Design

In the typical four-cylinder engine under discussion, the crankshaft is supported in the crankcase by three main bearings. The crankshaft of a multi-cylinder engine is a somewhat elaborate and expensive component as might well be expected from the arduous task that it is made to perform. The crankshaft has to control the motion of each of the four pistons (*see* Fig. 3.3) and is subjected to very heavy fluctuating loads. The loading is a complex combination of bending and twisting and the crankshaft must be well designed and of good quality in order to withstand the high stresses. It is usually machined from a single steel forging but cast iron crankshafts are being increasingly used. Cast iron construction makes it possible to produce a light-weight crankshaft of economical proportions without excessive machining. A cast crankshaft is rather more liable to " fatigue " failure—fracture after prolonged running with a fluctuating load—but methods of reducing this risk are known. A separate illustration of a typical forged crankshaft is shown in Fig. 3.5. The three portions of the shaft rotating in the main (i.e. the stationary) bearings are described as journals. Each piston is connected to the crankshaft through a connecting rod whose two ends are described by the engineer as the big end and the small end (Fig. 3.6). The big end of each connecting rod is made in two parts so that it can be bolted around the crankpin of the crankshaft.

If the crankshaft were to be in direct contact with the cast iron of the main bearings or the steel of the big end, the friction and rate of wear would be very high. The main bearings and the big ends are therefore

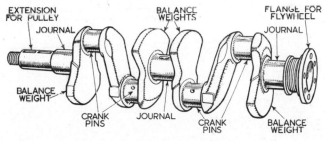

*Fig. 3.5. Crankshaft for a four-cylinder engine*

lined with special prefabricated bearing shells made in two halves. Shells of this type are illustrated in Fig. 3.6 and are discussed in more detail in the chapter on lubrication. The rotation of each crankpin and big end around the centre line of the journals tends to produce a large rotating force on the adjacent main bearings, just as swinging a weight on the end of a piece of string produces a force in the string. Added to this is the force required to accelerate the piston backwards and forwards. To counteract these forces and reduce the loads on the bearings balance weights are incorporated in the crankshaft webs opposite the big ends and next to the journals (Fig. 3.5).

The connecting rod is usually a steel stamping having an I-shaped cross-section between the two ends. The piston takes the form of a hollow cylinder, closed at the top end and open at the bottom. The piston is an aluminium die-casting and has two bearing holes or bosses formed in opposite sides; through these holes passes a steel tube known as the gudgeon pin. This pin passes through the small end of the connecting rod and is made hollow in order to reduce the reciprocating weight. If the gudgeon pin is free to rotate in both the piston and the small end, it is said to be fully floating.

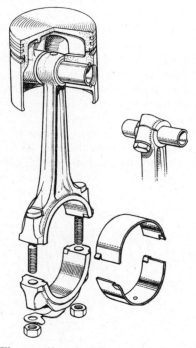

*Fig. 3.6. The connecting-rod big end is lined with a pair of thin shell bearings whose inside surfaces produce low friction. The small-end gudgeon pin may be either fully floating (left) or clamped (right)*

The small end of the connecting rod is lined with a bronze tube or bush to reduce wear and the gudgeon pin is prevented from moving sideways and scouring the bore by a pair of spring clips fitting into internal grooves in the piston bosses. An alternative arrangement is for the gudgeon pin to be clamped in the connecting-rod small end in which case the bush and spring clips are not required; but the first arrangement is generally regarded as more satisfactory in that it reduces wear on the piston and does not entail weakening the small end of the connecting rod to provide a clamp.

Since the piston must be gas-tight in the cylinder yet still slide up and down freely, two contradictory requirements have to be satisfied. As the piston expands more than the cylinder when it gets hot, the piston diameter must be rather less than the cylinder bore. The piston is therefore fitted with sealing rings which prevent the leakage of the hot gases downwards and of lubricating oil upwards. These piston rings lie in ring grooves formed in the outside of the piston and are of rectangular section. They are made of cast iron which is springy and wears well and are made slightly larger in diameter than the cylinder bore. The rings are cut across at one point leaving a gap which almost closes when the ring is compressed into the cylinder. Two or three plain rings are fitted near the top of the piston; these are called compression rings since their main function is to seal the piston against the gas pressure. The number of rings required for an effective seal tends to increase as compression ratios become higher. Beneath the compression rings and just above the piston bosses is another ring known as the scraper or oil-control ring whose function is to prevent oil from

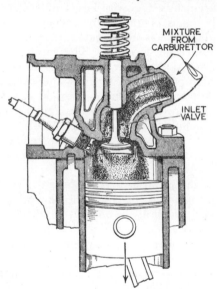

*Fig. 3.7. The mixture reaches each cylinder from the inlet manifold via passages in the cylinder head. Similar passages are provided for the escape of the exhaust gases*

entering the combustion space in excessive quantity. The piston rings will be dealt with further in the discussion of lubrication (Chapter 8).

The way in which the air enters the cylinder through the side of the cylinder head and past the inlet valve can be seen from Fig. 3.7, and the exhaust gases leave via the exhaust valve in a similar manner. As in the single cylinder engine described earlier, the valves control the admission and ejection of the gases to and from the cylinder by opening and closing at the required moments. Each valve is mushroom-shaped with a flattish head merging in an easy curve into a narrow stem which

27

slides in the cylinder head. The valve head is provided with a conical surface which sits on a conical seat in the cylinder head when the valve is closed. It is essential that the valve should be gas-tight and the valve and seat must therefore be very accurately manufactured. Each valve should really be lapped into its individual seat—that is, rotated on its seat in the presence of an abrasive paste—until the two parts match, but the need for economy often prevents this operation from being performed thoroughly. The valve seat may be the cylinder head itself or the head may be fitted with an insert which can be replaced when worn. Similarly the valve stem may run directly in contact with the head (as in recent Ford engines) or a tubular valve guide may be inserted in the head; such a guide can be renewed when wear takes place. Direct contact is cheaper of course and the valve runs cooler but wear can only be counteracted by providing special replacement valves with larger diameter stems.

The cams operating the valves are formed on a single shaft which runs in bearings in the side of the crankcase, parallel to the crankshaft but somewhat above it. The camshaft, as it is called, is chain-driven from the crankshaft at half crankshaft speed, as can be seen from Fig. 3.3. On high-performance engines the camshaft is often gear-driven. As a cam rotates, it lifts the cylindrical cam follower or tappet in its guide. The motion is transmitted through the long pushrod to a lever or rocker arm mounted on the rocker shaft. The opposite end of the lever therefore descends and the valve is forced open. Whilst the extremity of the cam is in contact with the tappet, the valve remains open, but as rotation continues the valve closes under the action of its spring. One end of the spring is fixed against the cylinder head whilst the other end presses against a collar attached to the top of the valve stem. Sometimes two springs are used, one within the other, a procedure which helps to avoid unwanted vibrations. The spring serves also to keep the tappet in contact with the cam when the cam is descending. Each valve has its own cam, tappet, pushrod and rocker arm, the rockers all being carried on a single rocker shaft which is mounted in bearings on top of the cylinder head.

When a tappet is resting on the low constant-radius part of its cam, the valve should be firmly closed. If the pushrod were slightly too long the valve might be unable to close completely. A screw adjustment is therefore provided at the end of the rocker arm next to the pushrod and the screw is adjusted to give a slight gap when the valve is closed. If the gap is too small it may disappear completely when the engine is hot due to thermal expansion and the valve would be prevented from closing properly; on the other hand, too large a gap leads to noisy operation and an increased rate of wear. On the engine shown in

Fig. 3.2 the upper parts of the pushrods are housed in steel tubes inserted in the cylinder block. The tubes are lower in weight than the extra material that would be required if the cylinder block were made to encase the pushrods completely. The valve gear is made as light as possible in order to reduce the load on the cams and keep the opening and closing time of the valves as short as possible. The pushrods are light and slender and the tappets are usually made hollow.

If the exhaust and inlet valves are spaced alternately from front to rear on the engine, each exhaust and inlet port must be provided with

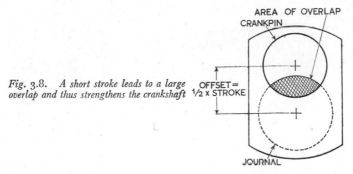

*Fig. 3.8. A short stroke leads to a large overlap and thus strengthens the crankshaft*

its own branch into the appropriate manifold, making eight branches in all. Sometimes the number of branches is reduced by altering the valve order in the following way. Writing E for an exhaust valve and I for an inlet valve, the arrangement for the four cylinders from front to rear is (E—I), (I—E), (E—I), (I—E). With this arrangement the inlet ports of cylinders 1 and 2 and those of cylinders 3 and 4 can be " siamesed " inside the cylinder head and led to single manifold branches. Similarly, the exhaust ports of cylinders 2 and 3 can be siamesed and the total number of branches is reduced from eight to five. However, the " breathing " of the engine is more restricted than with separate ports.

Vaporization of the petrol droplets in the mixture is assisted by providing a contact surface or " hot spot " between the inlet and exhaust manifolds. Sometimes the flow of the exhaust gases in the vicinity of the hot spot is regulated by a thermostatically operated valve, so that the rate of heat transfer is reduced as the engine becomes warm.

Many engines nowadays are made with their cylinder " square ", that is to say the stroke or piston travel is roughly equal to the bore or piston diameter. As was explained in Chapter 2, the old taxation formula favoured long stroke engines, but under the flat tax rate the trend has been towards shorter strokes—to square and even " over square " engines. If the designer chooses a large bore, he can get the required power with a shorter stroke and consequently the piston speed is lower. The offset of the crankpin from the centre-line, which is equal to half the stroke, is also reduced leading to a more rigid crankshaft (*see* Fig. 3.8). These advantages are counterbalanced to some extent by the higher gas load on the piston that accompanies a larger bore and by the increased length of the engine. A method sometimes adopted to permit a larger bore without increase in length is to siamese the cylinder bores. Instead of having cooling water circulating all around

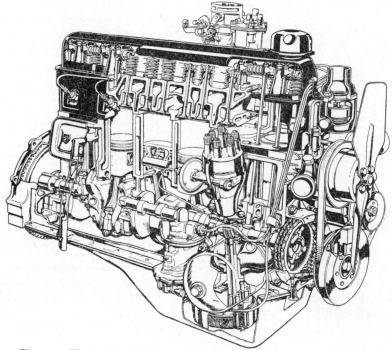

*Fig. 3.9. The Ford 6-cylinder, overhead valve engine. The gear drive for the distributor and oil pump is prominent; the cam-operated petrol pump is slightly to the left*

each bore, adjacent bores are brought closer together and separated by a solid wall.

Although it is the four-cylinder engine that has been described above, the basic design of a six-cylinder engine of this type is very similar (Fig. 3.9). Indeed, manufacturers sometimes produce four- and six-cylinder versions of the same basic design. The design of the crankshafts is of course very different but this point will be dealt with in Chapter 4.

An OHV engine of this type costs rather more to produce than a side-valve engine but its steady growth in popularity until it has all but eclipsed its former rival is due to certain solid advantages. Adjustment of the tappet clearances is a very simple operation since the valve gear is easily accessible. Decarbonizing, that is cleaning of the valves and the combustion space, is readily carried out since the cylinder head and valve gear can be detached as a unit and taken to a bench. Also, the compact combustion chamber of the OHV engine permits fairly high compression ratios to be used without excessive pinking and leads to greater fuel economy.

**The Silencer**

When the exhaust valve opens at the end of the expansion stroke, the pressure in the cylinder is still considerably greater than atmospheric. If the exhaust port discharged directly to atmosphere, the noise would be comparable to that caused when the gases explode from the end of a pistol behind the bullet. The pressure would be less but as the process is continuously repeated at high speed, the net result would be deafening —more like a small, high speed machine gun. On a multi-cylinder engine, the noise can be considerably reduced by discharging all the exhaust ports into a single branched pipe or manifold so that the exhaust flow becomes more smooth and continuous. But the resulting noise level still exceeds the " reasonable " level permitted by the law and the exhaust gases must therefore be passed through a silencer before escaping to atmosphere through the exhaust pipe. Silencing inevitably leads to some loss in engine power since anything that restricts the escape of the exhaust gases also tends to reduce the amount of fresh charge entering the cylinder. However, one shudders to think what life in our towns would be like if all motor cars were silenced as ineffectively as numerous motor cycles and scooters. A great deal of silencing is possible without serious loss of power and the noisiest engine is not necessarily the most powerful.

# Chapter 4

---

# ENGINE DESIGN FEATURES

IN the last chapter, a typical popular overhead-valve engine was discussed in some detail. The scope for variations in engine design, however, is very great, not only in detail but also in general construction. In the present chapter some of the more interesting design features of other engines are discussed. The first section on combustion chamber design covers alternative valve arrangements and the side-valve engine. Alternative cylinder arrangements such as the V type of construction are discussed in the next section. Then we deal with the design of the crankshaft and the choice of the firing order—why in fact the crankshaft is made the shape it is. This is followed by a few remarks on valve timing, which is particularly important in determining the character of an engine. Throughout the book, emphasis is placed on the important four-stroke engine. The principle and relative merits of the two-stroke engine are discussed at the end of the present chapter.

## Combustion Chamber Design

The performance of an engine depends to a great extent on the design of its combustion chamber—that part of the engine, enclosed by the piston crown, the cylinder walls and the cylinder head, in which combustion takes place. Clearly the combustion chamber is not a separate component which can be designed in isolation from the rest of the engine; its shape depends very largely on the design of the cylinder head, the location of the inlet and exhaust valves, and the ratio of bore and stroke.

In the side-valve engine, illustrated in Fig. 4.1(a), the valves are located in the cylinder block at the side of the engine. This arrangement results in very much simpler valve gear than is required in an overhead-valve engine since the pushrods, rocker arms and rocker shaft are eliminated; the side-valve engine is therefore cheaper to produce. Unfortunately it fails to satisfy one of the basic requirements for an efficient combustion chamber, namely, compactness; the more compact the combustion chamber, the lower the surface area of the walls and the lower the heat loss to the cooling water. A compact combustion chamber, like the overhead-valve design shown in Fig. 4.1(*b*), tends to produce an efficient engine in which more of the petrol energy is converted into useful power and less into heat; the m.p.g. is relatively high and the radiator can be smaller.

A compact combustion chamber has the additional advantage of being less susceptible to " knocking " or " pinking ". This trouble occurs when a pocket of mixture remote from the sparking plug becomes overheated and explodes spontaneously before the advancing flame reaches it (the matter is discussed further in Chapter 7). By mounting the plug in a fairly central position in a compact combustion chamber, the distance

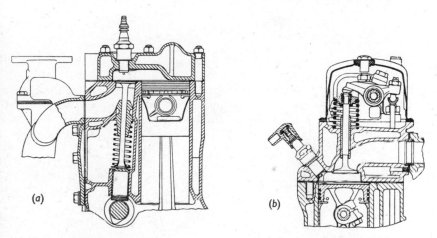

(a)

(b)

*Fig. 4.1.  A side-valve engine (a) has simpler valve gear than an overhead-valve design (b) but the combustion chamber is less compact. It is cheaper to produce though less economical to run*

to be travelled by the flame is reduced and conditions favourable to knocking are avoided.

Another way of reducing the tendency to knock is to make the flame spread more rapidly through the mixture so that all the mixture is burnt before any part of it becomes overheated. High flame speed can be encouraged by introducing " turbulence " into the mixture, stirring it up, as it were; the flame then tends to spread more rapidly to the adjacent unburnt particles of the mixture. The Vauxhall " squish " type of cylinder head, illustrated in Fig. 4.2, shows one simple and effective method of promoting turbulence. When the piston approaches the top of its stroke, the mixture trapped between the piston crown and the lower part of the cylinder head is ejected towards the left at high velocity. High turbulence increases the rate of heat loss to the cylinder walls and

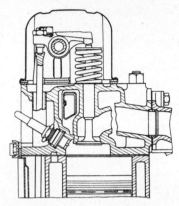

Fig. 4.2. *An OHV engine with " squish "-type combustion chamber for the promotion of turbulence*

it is therefore important not to produce more than is required to overcome the knocking tendency.

When an engine is run at full throttle, the power it delivers increases roughly in proportion to its speed over a fairly wide speed range. At very high speed, however, the maximum power obtainable is limited by the throttling effect of the inlet and exhaust valves on the air flow

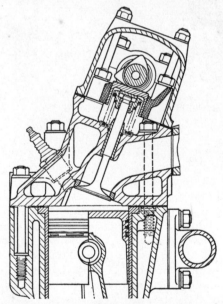

Fig. 4.3. *Coventry Climax engine with single overhead camshaft. The low weight of the valve gear permits very much higher engine speeds than are obtainable with an overhead valve engine using a side camshaft*

and by the inertia of the valve gear. On an overhead-valve engine with side camshaft the weight of the valve gear is considerable, and, at high speed, the cam force required to open the valves and the spring force required to close them is very large. If the weight of the valve gear can be reduced, the way is open to a further increase in engine

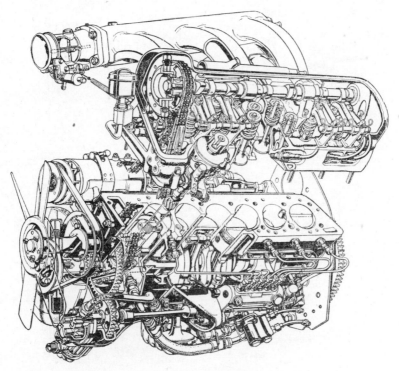

*Fig. 4.4. This Mercedes engine has its single overhead camshaft mounted nearly on the top of the valve stems. The rockers are pivoted at their ends and bend very little. No carburettor is used—the petrol is injected directly into each cylinder*

speed. On the Coventry Climax engine shown in Fig. 4.3, the valve gear is extremely light and simple. A single overhead camshaft operates the valves directly without the intervention of pushrods. No rocker arms are required as the cams operate the valve tappets directly. These tappets fit like thimbles over the valve stems and slide in guides in the cylinder head; the tappets are provided to avoid the side thrust that would otherwise be exerted by the cams on the valve stems.

The Mercedes engine (Fig. 4.4) also uses a single overhead camshaft but the valve gear and the combustion chamber design are very different

35

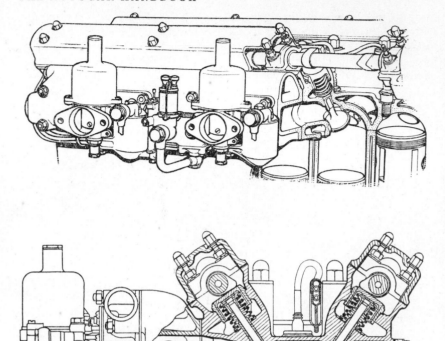

*Fig. 4.5.   Twin overhead-camshaft Jaguar engine with water-heated induction manifold and twin S.U. carburettors*

in conception.   The face of the cylinder head is flat and the combustion space is formed in the cylinder block itself.   The mating surface between the block and the head is cut at an angle and the piston crown is shaped to give " swish " effect between the crown and the cylinder head.

The Jaguar engine (Fig. 4.5) uses twin overhead camshafts, one for the inlet valves and one for the exhaust.   The combustion chamber is shaped like a segment of a sphere and combines compactness with large valve area.   The power obtainable from an engine depends on the rate at which it can be made to consume air and petrol.   Large inlet valves are required to avoid restriction of the mixture entering the cylinder and moderately large exhaust valves are needed to keep down the power wasted in expelling the exhaust gases from the cylinder. The overhead camshaft arrangement considerably reduces the weight of the valve gear and makes it possible for the valves to work more rapidly than with a side camshaft arrangement; thus the engine can run at higher speed, can consume the mixture more rapidly and can therefore develop greater power. The sparking plug is located centrally between the valves so that the path to be travelled by the flame is as short as possible. The inlet and exhaust manifolds are on opposite sides of the engine. Each inlet port is served by a separate branch from the manifold which draws the mixture from twin carburettors. The manifold is heated by circulation of the engine cooling water.

The Fiat engine (Fig. 4.6) is an example of how an (approximately) hemispherical combustion chamber with laterally opposed valves can be achieved using a single side mounted camshaft.

The Rolls-Royce combustion chamber (Fig. 4.7) makes use of overhead

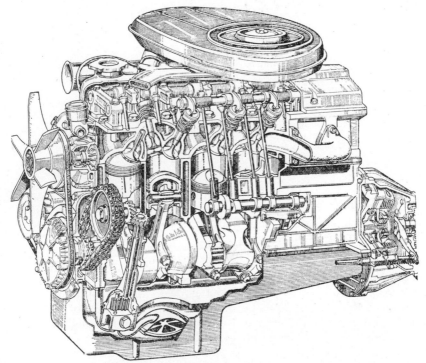

*Fig. 4.6. This 6-cylinder Fiat engine has its inlet and exhaust valves mounted on separate rocker shafts but uses a single camshaft*

37

inlet valves and side exhaust valves operated by a single side camshaft. Separating the valves in this way makes the use of large valve diameters comparatively easy. A certain amount of " squish " is used between the piston crown and the left-hand side of the cylinder head. The Rover engine (Fig. 4.8) is somewhat similar in design but various modifications have been ingeniously devised in order to produce a compact combustion

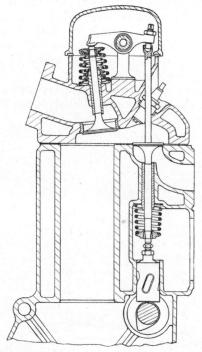

Fig. 4.7. *Rolls-Royce cylinder design with overhead inlet and side exhaust valves, operated by a single side-camshaft*

chamber. The bottom face of the cylinder head is inclined at an angle to the horizontal and the crown of the piston is shaped to promote " squish ".

### Cylinder Arrangements

For engine capacities up to about 2,000 c.c. the most popular arrangement consists of four cylinders arranged vertically in line. If more power is required than can readily be obtained from an engine of this size, it is usual to increase the number of cylinders to six. It would of course be possible to increase the power of a four-cylinder engine by increasing the size of the cylinders, but this approach is less satisfactory. If the engine cylinder becomes too large, various technical difficulties arise. It becomes more difficult to ensure rapid charging of the cylinders since the same number of inlet valves has to pass an increased quantity of mixture. Another difficulty is that the flame initiated at the sparking plug has a greater distance to travel. Also, the pistons become larger and heavier and the loads acting on the crankshaft tend to increase. If, therefore, the capacity of a 3,000 c.c. four-cylinder engine is to be increased, the power increase will be greater if two cylinders of the original size are added than if the capacity of the four cylinders is increased to 4,500 c.c. The six-cylinder engine will probably give at least 50 per cent more power whereas the larger four-cylinder engine will give rather less than a 50 per cent increase. Moreover, the six-cylinder engine, generally speaking, is smoother running since the crankshaft receives six moderate impulses from the pistons in the same time as the four-cylinder engine crankshaft receives four large impulses.

In Europe, the six-cylinder engine has proved capable of meeting most of the demand for greater engine power. The largest engines in general use have capacities in the region of 4,000–4,500 c.c. giving an

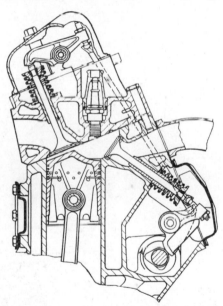

Fig. 4.8. *Rover combustion chamber with overhead inlet valves operated through push-rods and rockers and side exhaust valves operated through rockers only*

individual cylinder capacity of about 700 c.c. In America the power output demanded has increased to such an extent that the six-cylinder engine has been unable to meet the requirement. Larger cylinders would be undesirable for the reasons mentioned above and a further increase in the number of cylinders was therefore required. One possibility would be to add a further two cylinders to the block giving an

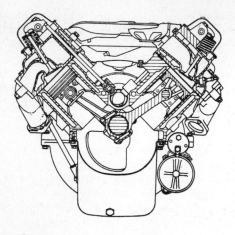

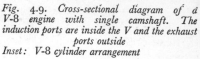

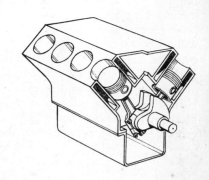

Fig. 4.9. Cross-sectional diagram of a V-8 engine with single camshaft. The induction ports are inside the V and the exhaust ports outside

Inset: V-8 cylinder arrangement

Fig. 4.10. (Below) The Rolls-Royce V-8 engine uses aluminium for the combined cylinder block and crankcase and also for the cylinder head. The pistons run in cast iron cylinder liners

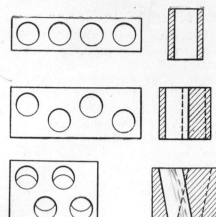

*Fig. 4.11. Four-cylinder Lancia engine with twin side camshafts and cylinders inclined in a narrow V Inset: Staggering the cylinders makes it possible to bring them closer together. A small V-angle is then required to bring the crankshaft in line with both pairs of cylinders*

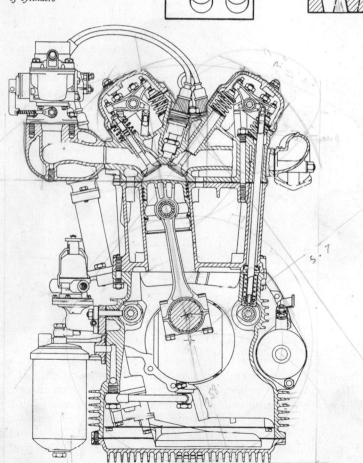

eight-cylinder, in-line engine; a " straight eight " engine as it is called. Such an engine can give a perfectly satisfactory performance but it makes heavy demands on space under the bonnet because of its excessive length. An alternative possibility, and the one which has been almost universally favoured in America, is to use the V-8 construction—that is, two banks of four cylinders arranged in the form of a V (Fig. 4.9). The two banks of cylinders are set at an angle of 90° to each other and the overhead valves of the two banks are operated through pushrods by a single camshaft located inside the V.

A British example of V-8 construction is offered by the Rolls Royce engine shown in Fig. 4.10. The connecting rod big ends of each pair of cylinders run side by side on the common crank pin and the two cylinder banks are slightly offset to allow for this.

The advantage of V construction is that it produces a shorter engine than the in-line arrangement since a pair of cylinders arranged in a V add no more length to the engine than a single vertical cylinder. Although V construction has been applied mainly to eight-cylinder engines, it has also been used successfully on four- and six-cylinder engines. On the four-cylinder Lancia engine (Fig. 4.11) the angle of the V is very small—some 10° compared with the 90° commonly used

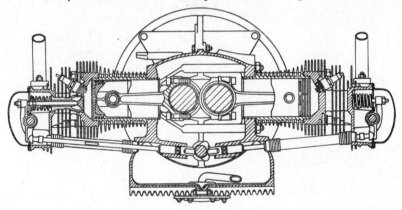

*Fig. 4.12. The Volkswagen " flat four " air cooled engine. Each cylinder consists of a finned iron barrel clamped between the cylinder head and the crankcase*

on V-8 engines. In fact the engine can equally be regarded as an in-line engine which has been modified for compactness. If we start with four cylinders in line, then before we can shorten the engine we must displace alternate cylinders to one side of the engine (*see* Fig. 4.11 inset). The bores can now be brought closer together, thus shortening the engine. The crankshaft is no longer vertically below the cylinders; the last modification is therefore to incline the four cylinders so that they form a narrow V with the crankshaft at the point of the V. This brings us to the Lancia arrangement. The engine uses two camshafts located on opposite sides of the crankcase. The valves of each cylinder are inclined at a wide angle to each other and are operated by different camshafts.

An alternative way of reducing the length of a four-cylinder engine is to use the " flat four " arrangement. The cylinders are placed hori-

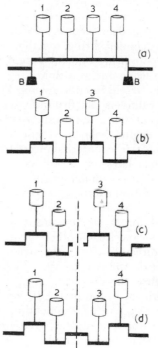

*Fig. 4.13. The 4-cylinder engine crankshaft
(a) This form would be simple to make but it is never used because it does not allow the firing of the cylinders to be spread out; and very heavy counterweights would be needed
(b) This form appears to be a possibility. The firing can be spread out, e.g. 1-2-3-4-1 . . .; and cylinders 2 and 4 balance cylinders 1 and 3
(c) Form (b) is really equivalent to two identical 2-cylinder engines, each of which is slightly out of balance
(d) By changing one half-engine in (c) round, we get the best crankshaft arrangement for a 4-cylinder engine*

zontally with two on each side of a central crankshaft. The air-cooled, rear-mounted Volkswagen engine is built as a flat engine (Figs. 4.12 and 9.2).

The General Motors flat six engine used on the small Chevrolet is also air-cooled and rear mounted.

### Firing Order and Crankshaft Design

The simplest shape of crankshaft for a four-cylinder, in-line engine would be that shown in Fig. 4.13(a). The crankshaft has a single " throw " to which all four connecting-rods are coupled. This simple design is never used in practice. owing to its two serious drawbacks. Firstly, all four pistons move in phase with each other and this is bound

THE AUTOCAR HANDBOOK

to cause unpleasant vibrations. The balance could be improved by attaching balance weights to the crankshaft at the points B but only the vertical forces can be balanced in this way; the rotation of the balance weights would introduce horizontal forces which would continue to cause vibration. The second disadvantage concerns the timing of the explosions. It is desirable that the cylinders should fire in order, one at a time, so that a smooth turning effort is produced. With this arrangement, however, individual firing is impossible. Every cylinder of a four-stroke engine fires once every two revolutions when the piston is at top dead centre. With this form of crankshaft, we can have all four cylinders firing together every other revolution; or we can have one pair firing one revolution and one the next; but we cannot have them firing one at a time.

The arrangement shown in Fig. 4.13(b) is a considerable improvement. The cylinders can fire individually, in order, at 180° intervals of crankshaft rotation; the firing order could be 1—2—3—4—1 . . . and so on. The engine balance is also improved since the downward motion of piston 1 is counterbalanced by the upward motion of piston 2. The balance however is still not perfect. The engine is really equivalent to two two-cylinder engines as shown in Fig. 4.13(c) and each of these half engines exerts a " turning " vibration on the engine. The explanation of this is quite simple: the inertias of the pistons 1 and 2 exert equal forces on the crankshaft but in opposite directions; the two forces cancel each other out to a large extent but as the two forces are not directly in line, the net result is to produce a fluctuating bending effect on the crankshaft. As the other half of the engine is identical to the first, the pistons 3 and 4 produce a similar bending effect which is additional to the first. If, however, pistons 3 and 4 are changed round as in Fig. 4.13(d), the bending effect due to 3 and 4 opposes the bending effect due to 1 and 2. We are left with the conventional four-cylinder crankshaft which provides the best balance that can be achieved in a four-cylinder engine. Two orders of firing are possible: 1—2—4—3 or 1—3—4—2. Clearly, 4 must be the third cylinder to fire since there has to be an explosion every half revolution and 4 reaches top dead centre one whole revolution after 1. The only choice therefore is whether 2 or 3 shall succeed 1. There is little to choose between the two alternatives; most manufacturers favour the order 1—3—4—2 but the other sequence is used by Ford on their four-cylinder engines.

Similar principles concerning balancing and explosion sequence apply to six-cylinder engines. With six cylinders firing every two revolutions, the angular spacing of the crankpins has to be $\frac{2 \times 360}{6}$ or 120° instead of 180° (Fig. 4.14). Starting at the front end the second throw comes

44

120° after the first, and the third comes 120° after the second. The rest of the crankshaft is a mirror image of the first half according to the balancing principle outlined above for the four-cylinder engine. The usual firing order adopted is 1—5—3—6—2—4 but other orders are possible. Six reaches top dead centre one revolution after 1 and must therefore be the fourth in order. Making 5 follow 1 helps to improve mixture distribution in the manifold. Either 3 or 4 could be made to

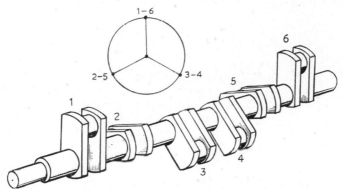

Fig. 4.14. The " throws " of a 6-cylinder crankshaft are spaced angularly at intervals of 120°. The usual firing order is 1-5-3-6-2-4-1 . . .

follow 5; choosing 3 avoids having two adjacent cylinders firing in succession. As 2 must follow one revolution after 5, and 4 one revolution after 3, the whole sequence is now determined.

### Valve Timing

When the firing order has been settled, the cams on the camshaft must be arranged to operate the valves in the same order. The firing order could only be changed from 1—3—4—2 to 1—2—4—3 by fitting a new camshaft and interchanging the leads to the sparking plugs.

Ideally, the inlet valve would open instantaneously at the end of the exhaust period and close instantaneously just after the beginning of the compression stroke. The flow of mixture through the valve does not stop immediately the piston reaches the bottom of its stroke, and by delaying the closing a larger charge is trapped in the cylinder. In practice, of course, the valve is operated by a cam and must open gradually. The valve begins to open when the point A on the cam arrives under the tappet (Fig. 4.15) and is not fully open until the cam has turned to the point B. The position of the crankshaft when the valve starts to open is fixed by the chain or gear drive of the camshaft from the crankshaft. Usually the inlet valve is timed to open 5–10° before the piston reaches top dead centre. Whilst the constant radius part

45

of the cam BC is passing, the valve remains fully open and at point C the cam starts to close. The cam may not be fully closed until 45° after bottom dead centre or even more on high speed engines (Fig. 4.15(a), (b) and (c) ).

The exhaust valve is timed to begin opening 50° or more before the end of the expansion stroke (Fig. 4.15(d) ). Very little power is lost by this early opening since the piston is already near the bottom of the

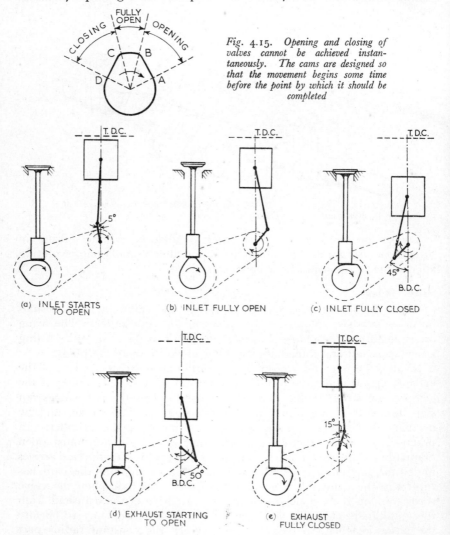

Fig. 4.15. Opening and closing of valves cannot be achieved instantaneously. The cams are designed so that the movement begins some time before the point by which it should be completed

(a) INLET STARTS TO OPEN

(b) INLET FULLY OPEN

(c) INLET FULLY CLOSED

(d) EXHAUST STARTING TO OPEN

(e) EXHAUST FULLY CLOSED

stroke and the cylinder pressure is low. If the opening were delayed, the piston might have to do more work forcing the exhaust gases through the partially open exhaust valve. Fig. 4.15(e) shows the exhaust valve fully closed some 15° after top dead centre. Late closing of the exhaust valve assists scavenging rather as late closing of the inlet valve assists charging.

### The Two-stroke Engine

Most of the petrol engines used in motor cars operate on the four-stroke cycle which was discussed in detail in Chapter 2. Unless otherwise stated, all reference to petrol engines in this book can be taken as referring primarily to four-stroke engines. It is, however, possible for a petrol engine to operate on a cycle consisting of only two strokes and, although this cycle is seldom used for medium and large size cars, it is quite popular on the small runabout type.

As we have seen, the strokes of the four-stroke cycle are: (1) suction, (2) compression, (3) expansion and (4) exhaust (*see* Fig. 2.2). Two revolutions of the crankshaft are required for a complete cycle of four strokes; consequently a firing (expansion) stroke only occurs in a given cylinder every other revolution. On the two-stroke cycle, the four processes are compressed into *two* strokes of the piston, i.e. one revolution of the crankshaft. The compression and expansion strokes occur much as in the four-stroke cycle, but the exhausting of the cylinder and the entry of the fresh charge are squeezed into a short period between the end of the expansion stroke and the beginning of the next compression stroke. As the piston approaches the lower end of the cylinder, it uncovers two ports in the cylinder wall. The exhaust gases escape through one port while a fresh charge of mixture is blown in through the transfer port opposite (Fig. 4.16(c) ). To prevent the fresh mixture from short-circuiting the cylinder and escaping through the exhaust port, the top of the piston is sometimes provided with a hump which directs the fresh charge towards the top of the cylinder. The angles of the ports can be arranged to give a similar effect.

The pressure for forcing the fresh charge into the cylinder can be provided by an engine-driven blower located between the carburettor and the inlet ports. The usual procedure on small engines, however, is to use the underside of the piston as a pump as shown in Fig. 4.16. When the piston rises it draws the mixture into the crankcase through a port connected to the carburettor (Fig. 4.16(a) ). As the piston falls, it covers the carburettor port and compresses the mixture in the crankcase causing a rise in pressure (Fig. 4.16(b) ). When it descends further, the piston uncovers the cylinder inlet port and the pressure in the crankcase forces the mixture into the cylinder. The remainder of the exhaust gases

47

are displaced from the cylinder by the entry of the fresh charge (Fig. 4.16(c) ).

Every time the piston rises, the mixture is compressed and ignited above the piston while a fresh charge is drawn into the crankcase below the piston. Every time the piston falls, the hot gases do work on the top of the piston while the next charge is being compressed below the piston. Firing occurs every revolution instead of every other revolution. At first sight, therefore, it would seem that a two-stroke engine ought to be twice as powerful as a four-stroke engine of equal size. In practice, the advantage is considerably less than this. The fresh charge tends to mix with the exhaust gases so that some of the exhaust gas remains in

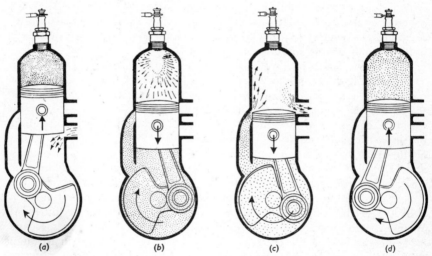

(a)          (b)          (c)          (d)

Fig. 4.16. In the 2-stroke cycle, the processes of compression, combustion, expansion, exhaust and suction are accomplished with two strokes of the piston and one revolution of the crankshaft
(a) Piston rises, compressing the mixture in the top of the cylinder and drawing a fresh charge into the crankcase
(b) The compressed mixture is ignited by means of a spark; hot gases drive piston downwards—work is done on crankshaft. Mixture below piston is compressed in crankcase
(c) Piston uncovers the exhaust port allowing the exhaust gases to escape and then uncovers the transfer port, allowing a fresh charge to enter the cylinder from the crankcase
(d) As the piston rises, the transfer and exhaust ports are again covered and the next cycle begins

the cylinder and some of the charge escapes through the exhaust. This has the double effect of reducing power and increasing fuel consumption.

The advantage of the two-stroke engine lies in its simplicity and cheapness. The elimination of independently operated inlet and exhaust valves greatly reduces manufacturing costs. Running costs, however, are higher owing to the higher petrol and oil consumption. Oil is not supplied separately to the crankcase but is mixed with the petrol when filling up. The engine therefore runs on a mixture of petrol and oil. An oily vapour pervades the crankcase, penetrating the big-end bearings and adhering to the cylinder walls. Lubrication is very much less efficient than that of a four-stroke engine with its pressure lubrication and the same long engine life cannot be expected. A two-stroke engine is generally very much noisier than a four-stroke and cannot operate smoothly over such a wide range of speed. It is difficult to fit an effective silencer without impeding the escape of the exhaust gases and reducing the effectiveness of the charging still further in comparison with the four-stroke engine. Most of the two-stroke engines used on baby cars have been developed from motor-cycle engines and are therefore air-cooled. It seems unlikely that two-stroke engines will ever be widely used for larger sizes of car because of the disadvantages mentioned. Only when cheapness, simplicity and light weight are of prime importance can the two-stroke take the place of the four-stroke. Its main application, therefore, seems likely to remain confined to light weight motor cycles, scooters and mopeds.

**Chapter 5**

# PRODUCING THE MIXTURE

IT has already been explained in Chapter 2 that to burn 1 lb of petrol requires about 15 lb of air. For a petrol engine to deliver maximum power the mixture must be rather richer in petrol whilst for maximum economy the mixture should be on the weak side, but by and large the mixture strength must be maintained somewhere around 15 to 1—the exact mixture depending on the actual operating condition. If it is not, then the fuel consumption of the engine may be excessive or its maximum power may be limited, or worse still the engine may not run at all. On the vast majority of petrol engines the mixture strength is regulated by a carburettor and the main part of this chapter is devoted to a discussion of this vital component. Nowadays the fitting of an air cleaner to the carburettor makes the mixture producing section of the engine particularly prominent (*see* Fig. 3.1). Air filters and silencers, supercharging and petrol injection are discussed later in the chapter.

**The Constant Choke Carburettor**

The carburettor diagrammatically shown in Fig. 5.1, is of the downdraught type, meaning that the air and mixture are drawn vertically downwards into the inlet manifold of the engine, but the operating principle applies equally to horizontal and other types. The majority of carburettors, including those of Solex and Zenith manufacture, operate on the " constant choke " principle (also referred to as " fixed choke "). The word " choke " is somewhat confusing because it has a dual meaning. " Choke " in the expression " constant choke " refers to the constriction or throat placed in the main passage of the carburettor through which all the air to the engine passes. This constriction, which is known as the choke tube or venturi, curves sharply inwards to form the throat and then tapers out more gradually. The other meaning of the word choke refers to the strangler device used for cold-starting on many carburettors; we return to this subject later in the chapter.

The downward motion of the engine piston during the suction stroke causes the cylinder pressure to fall and the pressure of the atmosphere

50

forces air through the carburettor and into the cylinder. At the end of the suction stroke the inlet valve closes, but as each cylinder in turn goes through its suction stroke the flow through the carburettor is fairly steady. Owing to the contraction of the carburettor passage size, the velocity of the air must increase as it flows towards the throat. This velocity increase can only take place if there is a pressure acting in the direction of flow—in other words, the pressure of the air must fall as the air approaches the throat. The petrol outlet is located in the throat at the same level as the petrol stored in the float chamber to which it is connected. The air in the float chamber is at atmospheric pressure and petrol is therefore forced along the connecting tube, through the jet and into the choke tube. As the air is moving at high speed the petrol stream is broken up into droplets and swept downwards into the inlet manifold.

The float chamber unit is designed to maintain a constant-level reservoir of petrol. If the level in the chamber falls, the float also falls,

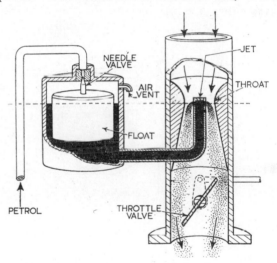

*Fig. 5.1. A simple carburettor. The low air pressure at the throat causes petrol to flow from the float chamber*

opening the needle valve and allowing more petrol into the float chamber. This causes the float to rise, thus sealing the float valve again; in this way the petrol level is kept very nearly constant.

The size of the petrol jet fixes the petrol flow rate for a given rate of air flow. If the jet size is correct, the mixture strength will have the required value and the engine will run satisfactorily under these conditions. Before considering the effect of engine speed and throttle opening on the mixture strength, a few words should be said about the throttle valve itself. The throttle valve is used to control the power delivered by the engine. It consists of a disc, roughly circular, of about the same diameter as the main air passage of the carburettor and it is located between the petrol outlet and the engine side of the carburettor. The spindle around which the valve turns is linked to the accelerator pedal so that when the pedal is depressed the valve opens and when the pedal is released the valve almost completely closes. The throttle valve acts simply as a variable obstruction between the atmosphere and the engine cylinders, by means of which the amount of mixture drawn into the cylinders can be controlled. The engine power depends directly on the amount of mixture admitted to the cylinders and the throttle valve therefore provides an extremely simple, cheap and effective means of controlling engine power.

Let us now consider how the mixture strength is affected when the throttle valve is opened wider or the engine speed is allowed to increase. The first effect in either case is to increase the rate at which air is drawn

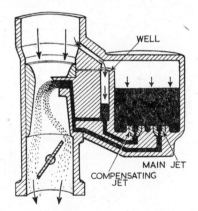

WELL

MAIN JET

COMPENSATING JET

*Fig. 5.2. Principle of Zenith compensating jet.*
*As engine power increases, flow of air into the well*
*restricts the flow of petrol from the compensating jet*
*and prevents the mixture becoming too rich*

through the choke tube. The velocity at the throat is therefore increased and the pressure falls still further. Thus the pressure difference across the petrol jet increases and more petrol is ejected. Simple theory shows that the velocity of the petrol flowing from the jet is proportional to the velocity of the air through the choke tube and therefore the mixture strength should remain constant regardless of throttle setting or engine speed. In theory, therefore, a simple carburettor such as this provides all the essential features, but, as we shall see, various modifications and additional features are required in practice to ensure satisfactory operation under all conditions.

### The Need for Mixture " Compensation "

A simple carburettor of the type shown in Fig. 5.1 does not in fact give constant mixture strength but delivers a mixture of increasing richness as the air flow increases. There are two main reasons for this tendency. Firstly, below a certain air flow, no petrol is delivered at all, partly because the petrol outlet must in practice be slightly above the petrol level in the float chamber in order to prevent leakage and partly because of the tendency of the petrol to cling to the jet. The mixture becomes progressively richer as these effects are overcome. The second reason is connected with the lower density of air in the choke tube at high air speed due to the reduced air pressure. The air flow is in direct proportion to the density whereas the petrol flow is influenced less strongly. The weight of petrol delivered therefore becomes relatively greater in relation to the air flow, i.e. the mixture becomes richer. Some additional feature must therefore be incorporated in order to control or " compensate " the mixture.

### Use of Compensating Jet and Air Bleed

The Zenith carburettor, shown in Fig. 5.2 in simplified form, achieves mixture compensation by means of a separate compensating jet. Both the main and compensating jet are located in the base of the float chamber. The main jet functions in a similar way to the jet in the simple carburettor described above but is smaller in size. The compensating jet, however, communicates with a small well or reservoir as well as with the main outlet and this reservoir, like the float chamber, is subject to the full atmospheric pressure in the inlet side of the carburettor. With the throttle valve closed the well is full of petrol, but when the throttle valve is opened, the reduced pressure in the throat causes the petrol in the well to be forced out into the choke tube producing a temporary richening of the mixture. This richening during acceleration is useful in preventing the momentary loss of power or " flat spot " that tends to occur when the throttle valve is opened and the air flow increases faster than the petrol. When all the petrol in the well has been expelled, air continues to flow into the well from the top and leaves through a passage at the base of the well where it mixes with the petrol from the compensating jet. This air flow tends to restrict the flow of petrol from the compensating jet. Thus the compensating jet and the air bleed associated with it introduce a tendency towards a weaker mixture at higher air flows and this offsets the tendency of the main jet towards a richer mixture. The flow of air from the well into the petrol stream

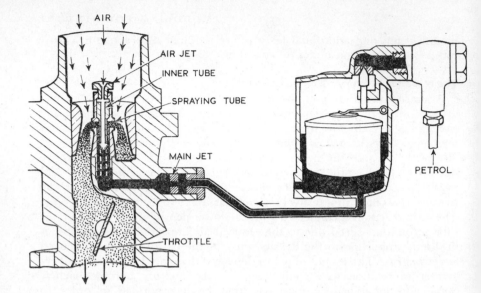

*Fig.* 5.3(*a*). *Solex progressive air bleed. As engine power increases, more air flows into the air jet, preventing the mixture becoming too rich*

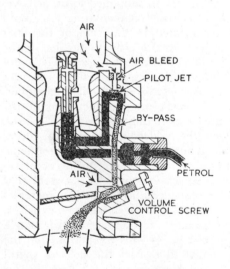

*Fig.* 5.3(*b*). *Idling mixture system. Petrol and air are drawn through a by-pass passage instead of from the main system*

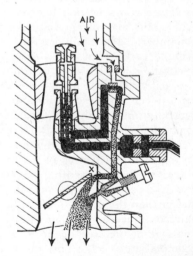

*Fig.* 5.3(*c*). *Low power operation. At small throttle openings, mixture is drawn from the upper hole as well, thus preventing a "flat spot" before the main system comes into operation*

has a further beneficial effect in that it helps to break up the petrol spray into fine droplets and so helps to achieve rapid vaporization.

### Progressive Air Bleed

The Solex carburettor achieves mixture compensation by using the main jet in conjunction with a progressive air bleed device which may be explained by referring to Fig. 5.3(a). Petrol from the float chamber flows through the main jet into the spraying tube and enters the throat of the choke through the delivery holes. An inner tube runs down the centre of the spraying tube and air from the carburettor inlet is able to enter this tube through an air jet. A series of small holes are drilled in the lower part of the inner tube at various levels through which air from the air jet passes and mixes with the petrol on its way to the delivery holes. At low throttle openings the amount of bleed air is fairly small; only the top air holes are uncovered and the bleed air does little to impede the flow of petrol. As the throttle opens the flow of bleed air through the air jet increases; air now begins to flow through the lower holes in the inner tube as well, producing a weakening effect to oppose the richening action mentioned above.

### Idling and Low Power Operation

Even with the compensating devices mentioned above, the mixture would not be satisfactory under all conditions, particularly during idling and at small throttle openings when the air flow through the carburettor is small. Under these conditions the air velocity in the choke tube is too low to cause the petrol to flow. Moreover, a rich mixture is required during idling to offset the low compression pressure and the larger quantity of exhaust gas that remains in the cylinder during compression. Even if petrol were to flow at the required rate, the air velocity would be too low to atomize the spray and much of the petrol would be deposited on the manifold walls. For these reasons, it is necessary to provide a separate means of supplying the mixture during idling and at small throttle openings.

The arrangement used on the Solex carburettor is shown in Fig. 5.3(b). When the engine is idling with the throttle valve closed, the pressure in the manifold on the engine side of the throttle valve is very low. A by-pass is provided in the carburettor body, allowing air to be drawn into the engine without passing the throttle valve. The size of the air bleed jet controls the amount of air flowing through the by-pass. Also situated in the by-pass is the pilot jet which is fed with petrol from the main petrol passage. The low pressure downstream of the throttle valve causes a mixture of petrol and air to flow into the engine manifold and the rate of flow can be controlled by adjusting the volume control screw.

55

During idling some of the air in the mixture emerging from the by-pass exit enters the by-pass through a second hole situated a little higher. Smooth, low-speed idling of the engine is achieved by adjusting the throttle stop screw (not shown) in conjunction with the volume control screw until a proper balance is achieved.

As the throttle valve is opened, it is most important that there should be no " flat spot " between the point at which the idling by-pass ceases to be effective and the point where the main spraying system comes into operation. The trouble is avoided by a reversal of the function of the upper hole (x) as the throttle valve opens (Fig. 5.3(c) ). When the tip of the throttle disc is near the hole a suction effect is created and mixture is now forced from this hole as well as from the lower hole. In this way, a progressive transfer of mixture supply from the idling to the main system is achieved.

### Starting

When starting from cold, the engine requires a particularly rich mixture since a large proportion of the petrol clings to the cold walls of the inlet manifold and cylinder walls and the petrol droplets evaporate rather slowly. One popular method of enriching the mixture at starting is the use of a " choke " or strangler. This is simply another butterfly valve, similar to the throttle valve, but located on the inlet side of the carburettor and manually operated by the driver. When the driver " pulls the choke out " he closes this strangler valve; usually the choke control is interconnected with the throttle-valve so that the throttle is opened slightly at the same time. In this way the petrol jets are subjected to a much greater suction and the petrol flow is greatly increased, so much so, that once the engine has fired the mixture is likely to be too rich for idling and the strangler has to be opened wider. The last operation is often achieved automatically by mounting the strangler disc in such a way that the air itself opens the valve to some extent as soon as the engine fires. Once the engine is tolerably warm, the choke control must be pushed right back, otherwise the mixture will be richer than is necessary for normal running; also the obstruction of the strangler valve will restrict the air flow and reduce the maximum engine power.

On some carburettors the choke control is completely automatic. When the engine is cold, the strangler valve is in the closed position. As soon as the engine fires, a small piston, operated by the depression in the intake manifold, causes the valve to open slightly. Then, as the engine warms up, a thermostat causes the valve to open completely. The thermostat consists of two strips of metal, fastened one against the other and wound into a coil. As they receive heat from the exhaust pipe, the two metals expand, but the inner strip is made of metal having a higher rate of expansion so that the coil unwinds and thus provides the motivation for the strangler valve.

Strangler devices are somewhat coarse in their action. A more refined starting device is the provision of what is, in effect, a separate miniature carburettor attached to the main instrument. One such device, of the type used on many Solex carburettors, is shown in Fig. 5.4. A separate supply of air is drawn through the starter air jet into the manifold, by-passing the throttle valve. The by-pass passage is supplied with petrol from the main float chamber but in order to enter the space and mix with the air the petrol must first pass the starter disc valve. This disc has two pairs of orifices drilled in it, one large and one small, and the disc can be manually rotated so that either pair is in line with the petrol passages. When the driver pulls the " choke " right out for starting, the larger pair is brought into line and a very rich mixture is produced. As soon as the engine fires the " choke " must be pushed to the half-way position thus bringing the smaller orifices into line. Once

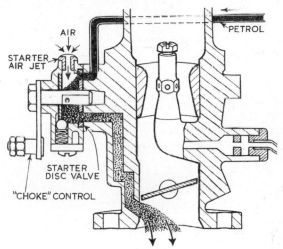

Fig. 5.4. *Solex starting device. When the " choke " is operated, mixture is drawn from a separate system at the side of the main instrument*

the engine has warmed up, the " choke " is pushed right in and the disc seals the passages off, putting the starting device out of action.

### Acceleration

During acceleration, following the opening of the throttle valve, it is desirable to inject an extra dose of petrol in order to avoid temporary weakening of the mixture and hesitation on the part of the engine. The most positive way of ensuring the extra charge is to provide an

3

acceleration pump which is brought into action when the accelerator pedal is depressed. The Zenith mechanical pump is illustrated in Fig. 5.5(a). When the throttle valve opens, the plunger is depressed and a charge of petrol is forced past the ball valve into the choke tube. The pump is only effective when the movement is sharp; during a slow movement, petrol can leak past the plunger and in this way unnecessary

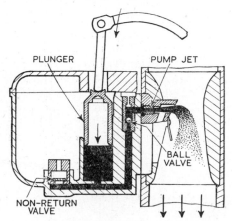

*Fig. 5.5(a). Acceleration. The Zenith mechanical pump causes a richening of the mixture when the throttle pedal is depressed prior to acceleration*

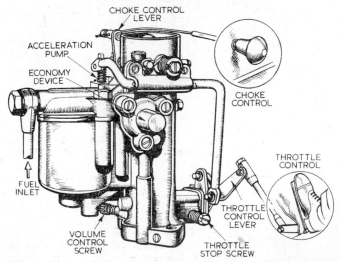

*Fig. 5.5(b). A Zenith carburettor fitted with a mechanical pump for acceleration and a " strangler " type of choke for starting*

injection is avoided. The pump is recharged during the up-stroke by flow of petrol from the float chamber through a non-return valve. The space above the ball valve is vented to the atmosphere to prevent petrol from flowing from the pump jet during steady running. An incidental advantage of this type of pump is that it can be useful in ensuring a good start when the engine is really cold. A few flicks of the accelerator pedal before starting the engine ensures a rich mixture in the inlet manifold. If, however, the engine were hot, the same action would probably result in over-richness and an inability to start. The link between the throttle control and the pump can be seen in Fig. 5.5(b).

On some Solex carburettors, the acceleration pump is not linked to the throttle but is actuated by the manifold pressure. When the throttle valve is partly closed, the manifold depression causes a diaphragm in the pump to be drawn against a spring and to draw in a charge of petrol. Immediately the throttle is opened wide, the depression collapses and the spring is released causing a charge of petrol to be injected into the induction pipe.

### The Constant Vacuum Carburettor

All the above discussions have been concerned with the constant-choke type of carburettor. There is a second class of carburettor in which the choke area is varied whilst the depression acting at the jet remains constant. The popular S.U. carburettor belongs to this class and a simplified illustration is given in Fig. 5.6. The area of the throat of the carburettor is varied by means of a piston and plunger unit which slides up and down vertically. The vent in the engine side of the plunger exposes the top of the piston to the suction pressure at this point. The space below the piston is vented to the atmosphere through a small hole. The carburettor has a single jet supplied with petrol from the float chamber but the effective size of the jet is varied by means of a tapered needle attached to the base of the plunger. When the throttle valve is opened, greater suction is exerted by the engine on the vent and the pressure above the piston falls momentarily. The atmospheric pressure on the other side of the piston remains constant, of course, and the plunger therefore rises until the balance has been restored. The throat area is thus increased and more air is admitted whilst at the same time the tapered needle rises and the fuel flow is increased. The taper form of the needle is carefully designed to give the required mixture strength over the whole range of operation. The air velocity through the throat is high enough over the range of operation to ensure good atomization of the fuel. Other advantages of this type are its rapid response during acceleration and the fact that the throat is opened wide at full throttle so reducing the pressure loss through the carburettor and increasing maximum power. These advantages make this type of carburettor particularly suitable for high performance sports cars.

### Petrol Injection Compared with the Carburettor

The modern carburettor is a reliable and fairly cheap instrument but it has several shortcomings which have led engineers to look for an alternative method of producing the mixture. The most promising alternative is some form of petrol injection but before discussing this system a few words should be said about the disadvantages of the carburettor.

A single carburettor often has to serve four or six cylinders and it is very difficult to ensure that each cylinder gets its fair share of both air and petrol. Some cylinders may be running weak and others may be running rich, whilst none is running at the most economical mixture strength. Furthermore, the carburettor throat restricts the flow of air to the engine and hence the power developed, since the maximum

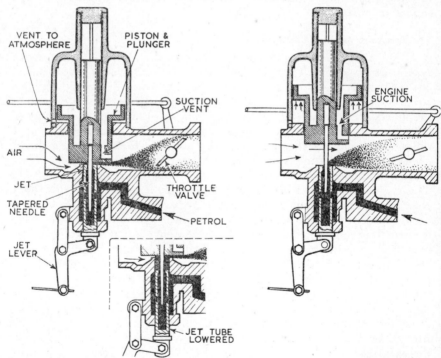

*Fig. 5.6. S.U. constant vacuum carburettor. Flow from the jet is controlled by a tapered needle attached to a plunger which rises when the throttle valve is opened. The flow can be independently increased for starting by lowering the jet tube*

power of an engine is limited mainly by the amount of air that the engine can consume. The maximum power can be increased by using a larger throat or by fitting two or more carburettors. In this way, the resistance to flow caused by the throat restriction is reduced and the maximum air flow and power are increased. Unfortunately, the economy at low power suffers, since the increased throat area results in low air velocity and the petrol spray in the throat is less effectively controlled and atomized. Twin or multiple carburettors help to provide uniform mixture distribution between the cylinders but they require careful

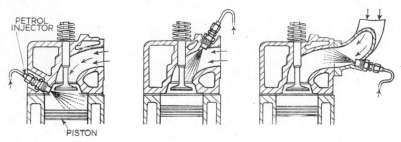

*Fig.* 5.7. *Petrol injection. Petrol can be injected either directly into the cylinder or the inlet port or the manifold branch*

matching; also, there is still some loss of power due to throat restriction and some sacrifice of part-load economy due to low throat velocity. Moreover, as the number of cylinders per carburettor is reduced, the pressure fluctuation at the jets increases making it more difficult to control the petrol flow.

The basic principle of petrol injection is that each cylinder is provided with its own injection nozzle which receives its correct amount of petrol from a special petrol pump system. The nozzle can be located so as to inject the petrol either directly into the cylinder or into the inlet port or into the manifold branch (*see* Fig. 5.7). When direct cylinder injection is used, the flow must be intermittent and the timing must be arranged so that injection only occurs during the suction and compression strokes. This can be achieved either by using a timed plunger pump of the diesel engine type (as on the Mercedes engine, Fig. 4.4) or by using a steady delivery pump in conjunction with timed injection nozzles. Intermittent injection can also be used with port and manifold injection locations but it is not essential. In the General Motors system fuel is injected continuously into the inlet port towards the inlet valve.

The mixture strength requirements of the engine are the same with petrol injection as with a carburettor and the petrol flow must therefore be related to the air flow under all conditions. Hence it is necessary to have a control system to regulate the petrol flow in response to changes

61

in air flow. With an intermittent injection pump, driven by the engine, the petrol delivery automatically increases with engine speed; changes in air flow due to varying the throttle opening can be allowed for by making the pump delivery respond to changes in manifold pressure between the engine and the throttle valve. On the General Motors continuous flow system, the fuel delivery rate is adjusted to the air flow rate by making it respond to the depression in a venturi on the atmospheric side of the throttle valve.

Petrol injection gives both higher maximum power and lower cruising petrol consumption. The main barrier to the wider use of petrol injection

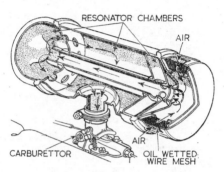

*Fig.* 5.8. *A combined air intake silencer and wetted wire air cleaner*

is the increased initial cost. The cost of the petrol injectors, fuel pump and fuel delivery control device is high compared with that of a carburettor. Nevertheless, the advantages of the system are considerable and it is being steadily developed and increasingly applied.

### Supercharging

A supercharger is a small air compressor which is used to pressurize the air intake of an engine and so increase the rate of air consumption. No engine, drawing air direct from the atmosphere, can consume a volume of air greater than the volumetric displacement of its pistons during suction. Owing to pressure losses in the carburettor and air intake and through the inlet valves, the volumetric efficiency may be less than 80 per cent and the power developed suffers accordingly. Superchargers are available which will boost the air inlet pressure by 6 or 7 pounds per square inch and increase the maximum power by 40 per cent or so.

The supercharger is normally fitted between the carburettor and the engine; the carburettor is not pressurized and functions in the normal way. The two main types of supercharger in general use are the Roots blower and the eccentric vane blower, but centrifugal blowers can also be used. The blower must be driven from the engine crankshaft, either through the fan belt or by separate gearing. The power absorbed by the blower is considerable, so not all the increased power developed by the engine is available at the road wheels. Supercharging increases the load on most parts of the engine and increased wear is likely to result. It also prevents the use of high compression ratios because the higher air inlet pressure increases the tendency towards knocking. Fuel consumption is higher than for an unsupercharged engine but the increase is not excessive in relation to the gain in power.

It seems unlikely that supercharging will be applied to popular vehicles more than at present. Its use properly belongs to those fields where maximum power from a given size of engine is the first consideration, e.g. motor racing and competition work. A manufacturer wishing to improve the performance of a particular model finds it more economic to increase the capacity of the engine and perhaps raise the compression ratio.

### Air Filtration and Silencing

In many countries of the world motor cars have to travel over long stretches of road where the surface is simply packed earth. Such roads are extremely dusty and a slight wind or a passing vehicle can raise a minor duststorm. Unless some reasonably efficient form of filter is used to clean the air before it enters the engine, the rate of wear in the cylinders and other parts to which the dirt-laden air penetrates is likely

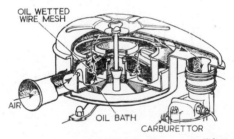

*Fig. 5.9. A combination of air intake silencer and oil bath air cleaner*

to be excessive. Even in this country with its carefully prepared road surfaces, elimination of dust prolongs the life of an engine and on all modern cars the carburettor draws its air through a filter. The same component can also be made to serve as an intake silencer, thus reducing the noise caused by the air-flow and the inlet valves.

A popular type of combined air filter and silencer is shown in Fig. 5.8. Air enters through a matrix of oil-wetted wire at one end of the cylindrical casing and the dust particles hit the wetted wire and tend to cling to the oil. Inside the cylinder, the surfaces are arranged to baffle and damp out any sound waves that travel back through the carburettor. Every 5,000 miles or so the wire matrix should be cleaned in paraffin or petrol and re-dipped in fresh engine oil.

The filter just described would rapidly become choked on really dusty roads and is only suitable for use under normal conditions. A more effective form of air cleaner employing an oil bath is shown in Fig. 5.9. Air enters the cleaner through a tube in the side of the outer casing and then flows vertically downwards through the circumferential gap between the side of the oil bath and an inner filter container. The sudden reversal in the direction of flow when the air enters the filter element causes the heavier dust particles to be precipitated into the oil bath. Some of the wet oil in the bath is picked up by the air stream and the filter element is therefore kept wetted and is able to attract the finer particles that have escaped the oil bath. Sludge gradually accumulates in the oil bath which must be emptied from time to time and replenished with fresh oil.

# Chapter 6

# PRODUCING THE SPARK

A four-cylinder engine propelling a car at 45 m.p.h. in top gear fires over 5,000 times every minute, each explosion being produced by passing an electric spark through the petrol-air mixture at the end of the compression stroke. If the sparking is irregular the engine will not run smoothly and much faulty operation can be attributed to faulty ignition. If the sparking fails completely the engine will not run at all, as demonstrated when the ignition switch is used for stopping the engine. An effective and reliable ignition system is therefore a first essential for any petrol engine. On nearly all modern engines the spark is produced by a coil and contact-breaker unit operating in conjunction with the battery. Most of the present chapter is therefore devoted to an account of this method. Magneto ignition, which was once predominant, is discussed briefly towards the end of the chapter.

### Need for High Voltage

Each cylinder of a modern petrol engine is fitted with a sparking plug and when the spark passes across the tip of the plug, the mixture of petrol and air starts to burn. If the plug is mounted centrally the flame will travel quickly through the mixture and the cylinder pressure will rise rapidly. The size of the spark is controlled by the gap between the electrodes at the tip of the plug (Fig. 6.1) and this is usually set to about 0·025 in. Although the gap between the electrodes is small, it offers a very high resistance to the passage of electricity. It is therefore necessary for a voltage of 10,000 volts or so to be applied to the plug if the required spark is to be produced. The voltage available at the battery, a mere 6 or 12 volts, is quite insufficient and a special high voltage system has to be provided. On most modern cars, an ignition coil, fed with current from the battery, forms the basis of the system.

### The Ignition Coil System

In order to understand how an ignition coil system works we must consider two fundamental principles concerning electricity and magnetism.

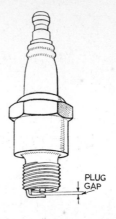

Fig. 6.1. *A typical modern sparking plug has a spark gap of about* 0·025 *in.*

Fig. 6.2(a). *(Below) A coil of wire carrying a current behaves like a magnet; it is often referred to as a solenoid or an electro-magnet*

PLUG
GAP

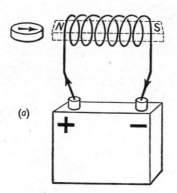

(a)

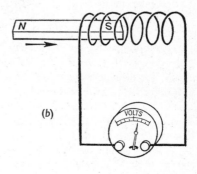

(b)

SPARK
GAP

Fig. 6.2(b). *(Above) When a magnet moves through a coil of wire an electric voltage is produced across the coil*

SECONDARY
COIL

PRIMARY
COIL

CONTACT
BREAKER

Fig. 6.3. *An ignition coil consists of two coils, one wound round the other. When the current in the primary coil is interrupted, a high voltage is induced across the secondary coil and a spark jumps across the gap*

Firstly, a coil of wire carrying a current creates a magnetic field as though a bar magnet were situated along its centre-line (Fig. 6.2(a) ). If a magnetic compass is brought near one end of the coil, the needle swings into line with the coil; when the current is turned off the needle swings back towards the north. The second principle concerns an effect which is roughly the opposite: when a magnet moves through a coil of wire a voltage is induced in the wire (Fig. 6.2(b) ). These two principles form the basis of the operation of dynamos, electric motors, transformers, electromagnets and so on, but our immediate concern is with the ignition coil.

An ignition coil is actually a combination of two coils, a primary coil and a secondary coil, as shown diagrammatically in Fig. 6.3. The primary winding is connected to the battery and carries a current which produces a magnetic field in accordance with the first principle above. When the contact breaker is opened the current dies away and the magnetic field collapses. This movement of the magnetic field has the same effect on the secondary coil as the movement of a magnet; therefore, in accordance with the second principle, a voltage is induced in the secondary winding and this voltage causes a spark to jump across the spark gap.

To ensure a high induced voltage in the secondary coil, various other features are employed. The two coils are wound round a central iron core which strengthens the magnetic field produced by the primary winding. Also the secondary coil is given about 40 times as many turns as the primary; this is because the voltage induced in a coil increases with the number of turns and a much higher voltage is required in the secondary than in the primary. The essential elements of an ignition coil system are shown in Fig. 6.4. The need for the condenser arises in the following way. To obtain a high voltage in the secondary coil, the magnetic field due to the primary current must change quickly; this means that the primary current must be made to die rapidly. The difficulty here is that the primary current tends to go on flowing across the contact points after the contact breaker has opened. This is because the collapse of the magnetic field also produces a self-inducing effect in the primary winding and the resulting voltage is sufficient to cause an arc across the points. Not only is the rate of change of current reduced but the rate of wear at the points is greatly increased. To overcome the difficulty the condenser is connected across the points. A condenser has the ability to store a charge of electricity and consists, in principle, of two metal plates separated by a thin layer of insulating material. In practice, the metal plates and the insulating layers, both of which are extremely thin, are wound into a spiral to make the condenser compact. At the moment when the points start to open, the electric charge on the

67

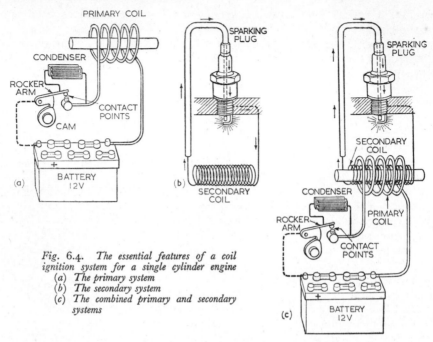

Fig. 6.4. *The essential features of a coil ignition system for a single cylinder engine*
(a) *The primary system*
(b) *The secondary system*
(c) *The combined primary and secondary systems*

condenser is zero and the condenser is therefore able to receive the current that would otherwise flow across the points. This enables the contact points to open without an arc being formed. Provided the condenser is not too large the voltage on the condenser quickly builds up, opposing the flow of current and causing it to die away rapidly. Thus, in addition to preventing arcing at the contact-breaker points, the condenser tends to produce a higher voltage in the secondary coil and to reduce the delay between the opening of the points and the passage of the spark at the plug.

The basic circuit diagram for a coil ignition system is given in Fig. 6.5. The sparking plug is automatically " earthed " by being screwed into the engine cylinder head. The circuit is completed by earthing the battery and contact breaker as well, i.e. connecting them to the engine or chassis. The coil connections shown are those used in practice and it will be seen that one of the secondary coil connections is connected to earth through the primary coil and the battery. The voltage across the sparking plug gap is therefore increased by this amount.

The construction of a modern ignition coil is shown in Fig. 6.6. The primary coil is wound outside the secondary coil in order to keep the primary winding cool. A 12-volt coil of this type has about 10,000 turns

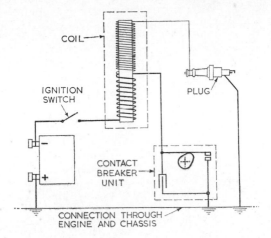

*Fig.* 6.5. *Ignition wiring diagram for a single-cylinder engine*

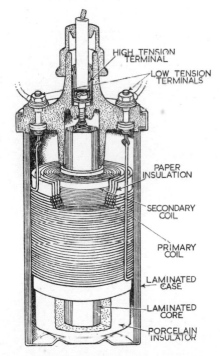

*Fig.* 6.6. *A modern ignition coil. The centre core is at a high voltage and has to be well insulated from the metal case*

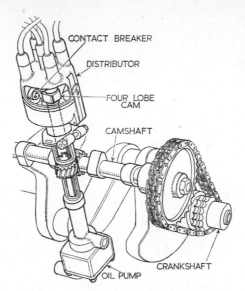

Fig. 6.7. *The distributor and the oil pump usually have a common drive from the engine camshaft*

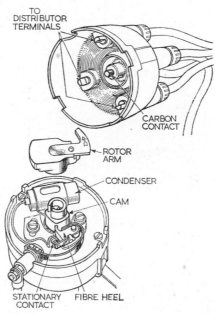

Fig. 6.8. *The distributor of a four-cylinder engine. The cam has four lobes and rotates at half engine speed*

in the secondary winding and about 250 turns in the primary, giving a "turns ratio" of 40 to 1. The coil windings must be insulated to withstand the high voltage—if the coil insulation breaks down, the engine is immobilized. The chief cause of insulation failure is moisture and coils are often immersed in oil and hermetically sealed to minimize the danger.

### The Contact Breaker and Distributor

A single-cylinder four-stroke engine fires once for every two revolutions of the crankshaft. The cam operating the contact breaker need therefore only rotate at half the crankshaft speed so that there is one spark for every two crankshaft revolutions. A four-cylinder engine, however, requires four sparks during two crankshaft revolutions and the contact breaker must therefore open and close four times. By placing four lobes on a single cam, the same coil and contact breaker can be made to provide the sparks for all four cylinders. As the main engine camshaft also rotates at half engine speed it is convenient for the contact-breaker drive to be taken from the camshaft through skew gearing as shown in Fig. 6.7. On most popular engines the drive is extended downwards to operate the lubricating oil pump in the manner shown. On some engines, the contact-breaker unit is mounted on the opposite side of the engine to the camshaft; the contact-breaker drive cannot, therefore, be vertical but must slope across the engine at an angle of 45° or so.

The four-lobe cam ensures that the correct number of high-voltage impulses is generated at equally spaced intervals but it is also necessary for these impulses to be applied in turn to the sparking plugs of the four cylinders. This requirement is achieved by the distributor which consists of a brass rotor arm rotating beneath four equally spaced terminals. The contact breaker and distributor are combined in a single housing as shown in Fig. 6.8, and the whole unit is loosely referred to as the distributor. The rotor arm is mounted on the contact-breaker spindle which extends beyond the four-lobe cam; thus the rotor arm also rotates at half engine speed. The high-tension lead from the coil is fed to a spring loaded carbon contact in the distributor head and this contact presses continuously against the centre of the rotor arm. The sparking plug leads are connected to the four terminals in the distributor head in the correct firing order. The rotor arm does not make actual contact with the terminals but rotates inside them with a small clearance. The gap is sufficiently small to offer low resistance to the high-voltage impulses from the coil and these are applied successively to each sparking plug.

The contact-breaker mechanism is mounted in the lower half of the distributor unit as shown in Fig. 6.8. One contact is carried directly on the stationary platform and is electrically earthed whilst the cam-operated contact is carried on an insulated spring lever which is connected to the low-tension coil. A fibre heel is attached to the lever part of the spring and presses continuously against the rotating cam. The spring serves the dual purpose of maintaining the closing pressure and acting

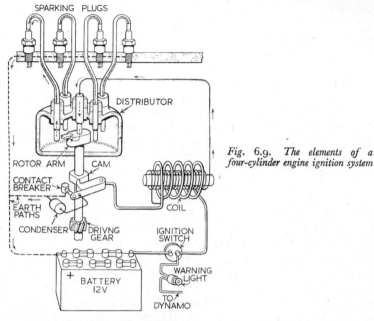

Fig. 6.9. *The elements of a four-cylinder engine ignition system*

as an electrical lead to the moving contact. A broken spring, therefore, causes both mechanical and electrical failure.

The contacts or points as they are usually called are made of tungsten to withstand the hammering and sparking. The gap between the points when the fibre heel is on top of the cam lobe is specified by the manu-facturer at somewhere between 12 and 18 thousandths of an inch depending on the particular design. If the gap is too small, the break will not be sharp and definite and the voltage induced in the high-tension coil will be low. If, however, the gap is too large, the time required for the points to close is increased and the current in the primary coil will not have sufficient time to grow to its full value in readiness for the next spark. The condenser is housed alongside the contact breaker, one side being earthed to the platform and the other connected to the moving contact via the spring.

The way in which the battery, coil, contact breaker, distributor and sparking plugs are interconnected on a four-cylinder engine is illustrated in Fig. 6.9. Apart from the use of a four-lobe cam in the contact breaker and the inclusion of the distributor, the wiring is the same as that shown earlier in Fig. 6.5. When the driver switches on the ignition, both the dynamo and the coil are connected to the battery and a small bulb lights up on the panel. As the bulb is in the dynamo circuit it can light up regardless of a break in the ignition circuit. Once the engine is running, the panel light goes out and only comes on again if the engine dynamo is not charging properly.

The ignition system of a six-cylinder engine can be arranged in precisely the same way using a six-lobe cam. Alternatively, two identical contact

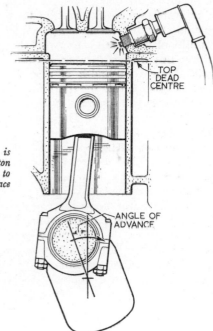

*Fig. 6.10. The ignition spark is timed to occur before the piston reaches top dead centre in order to allow time for combustion to take place*

breakers incorporated in a single distributor unit and operated by a special three-lobe cam may be used.

### Timing of the Spark

The electric spark across the sparking plug gap initiates combustion of the mixture. It is very important that the pressure rise due to combustion should take place when the piston is at the top of the cylinder (top dead centre). If the spark occurs too soon, combustion will take place before the compression stroke is complete and the pressure will

73

oppose the piston motion, so reducing engine power. If the spark occurs too late, the piston will have already completed a certain part of the expansion stroke before the pressure rise occurs and a corresponding amount of engine power will be lost. At first sight it would appear that the best moment for the spark would be at the end of the compression stroke but this is not so. There is always a small but definite interval of time between the passage of the spark and the attainment of maximum cylinder pressure. Part of the delay is due to the time required for combustion to start whilst the remainder is due to the time required for combustion to become complete.

The extent of the delay depends on many factors such as compression ratio, mixture strength, throttle opening, engine temperature and combustion-chamber design. Fortunately, it is moderately short—a few thousandths of a second—otherwise the petrol engine would be an impossibility; but when an engine is rotating at 2,000 r.p.m., say, even an interval of one thousandth of a second represents 12° of crankshaft rotation. Consequently the spark has to occur 20°, let us say, before the crankpin reaches its top point (see Fig. 6.10), that is, the points must open 20° before top dead centre. The distributor driving gear must be engaged with the corresponding gear on the engine camshaft in such a way that the contact-breaker cam is about to open the points when the crankpin is 20° before top dead centre. This angle is called the angle of advance and provision must be made for adjusting the angle to the best position by rotating the contact breaker relative to the central cam; for example, the whole distributor body may be provided with angular adjustment and locked in the best position when the engine is assembled. On most modern distributors, the plate carrying the contact breaker can be rotated within the body by turning a knurled nut at the side of the distributor thus providing further adjustment. This feature is incorporated with the automatic vacuum control described below and illustrated in Fig. 6.11(b).

### Automatic Ignition Timing

It has just been stated that, at 2,000 r.p.m., an ignition delay of one thousandth of a second corresponds to 12° of crankshaft movement. If, however, the speed is 1,000 r.p.m., the corresponding angle is only 6° and if the speed is 4,000 r.p.m. the corresponding angle is 24°. It is therefore necessary for the angle of ignition advance to increase as engine speed increases in order to allow sufficient time for combustion to take place. Modern distributors incorporate an automatic device which causes the angle of advance to increase as the engine speed rises. The contact-breaker cam is connected to the driving shaft through a coupling which incorporates two centrifugal weights (see Fig. 6.11(a) ).

As the engine speed rises, the weights fly out causing the cam to turn relative to the driving shaft in the direction of rotation.

The time required for combustion depends on the cylinder pressure at the end of compression; the lower the pressure, the longer is the

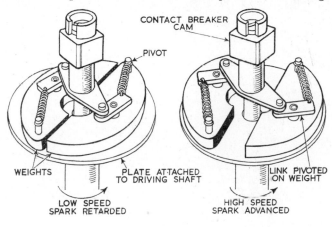

CONTACT BREAKER CAM

PIVOT

WEIGHTS     PLATE ATTACHED TO DRIVING SHAFT     LINK PIVOTED ON WEIGHT

LOW SPEED SPARK RETARDED     HIGH SPEED SPARK ADVANCED

*Fig. 6.11(a). (Above) At high engine speeds centrifugal weights acting on the contact breaker drive cause the spark to occur at a larger angle of advance*

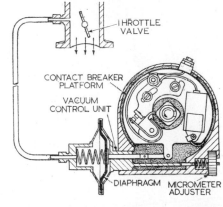

THROTTLE VALVE

CONTACT BREAKER PLATFORM

VACUUM CONTROL UNIT

DIAPHRAGM    MICROMETER ADJUSTER

*Fig. 6.11(b). (Right) Spark timing is also made to vary with induction pressure: at low throttle openings, the diaphragm moves to the left and the contact breaker points open earlier*

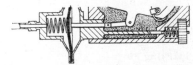

time required. The compression pressure varies considerably with throttle opening and engine speed and it is desirable that the angle of advance should vary correspondingly. Fortunately the compression pressure always varies in sympathy with the pressure in the induction manifold and the induction pressure can therefore be made to provide the basis of automatic control. A flexible diaphragm is incorporated in the distributor and subjected to the induction pressure by way of a small copper tube (*see* Fig. 6.11(b)). When the throttle opening is reduced the compression pressure is lowered and a larger angle of advance is required. The reduced induction pressure produces a " vacuum " effect on the diaphragm, and the atmospheric pressure on the other side of the diaphragm causes it to move outwards against the " vacuum ".

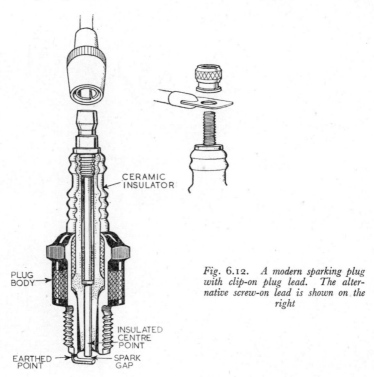

CERAMIC
INSULATOR

PLUG
BODY

*Fig. 6.12. A modern sparking plug
with clip-on plug lead. The alternative screw-on lead is shown on the
right*

INSULATED
CENTRE
POINT

EARTHED
POINT

SPARK
GAP

The diaphragm is coupled to the contact-breaker platform in such a way that a reduction in induction pressure increases the angle of advance.

### Sparking Plugs

The function of a sparking plug is to provide a pair of electrodes for the spark to jump across. A typical modern plug was illustrated in Fig. 6.1, and the internal construction of such a plug is shown in Fig. 6.12. The high-tension electrode runs through the centre of the plug whilst the " earthing " electrode is attached to the tip of the steel body. The electrodes are usually made of a nickel alloy but platinum tips may be used for extra durability. The body of the plug screws directly into the cylinder head so that the plug points project slightly into the combustion chamber. To ensure a gas-tight joint the sparking plug screws down on to a soft copper or copper and asbestos washer. Most modern cars are fitted with sparking plugs having a diameter over the threads of 14 mm, but 18 mm and 10 mm plugs are also in use. The length of the threaded portion is known as the " reach " of the plug and varies from $\frac{3}{8}$ to $\frac{3}{4}$ in. according to the particular engine design.

The high-tension lead from the distributor is often attached to the terminal at the top of the plug by means of a clip which springs over the terminal. Alternatively the lead is provided with a brass tab which is secured by a screw terminal as shown in Fig. 6.12. The high voltage of the central electrode is prevented from short-circuiting to " earth " by means of a substantial insulator. Most modern sparking-plug insulators are made from an aluminium oxide ceramic. The exposed

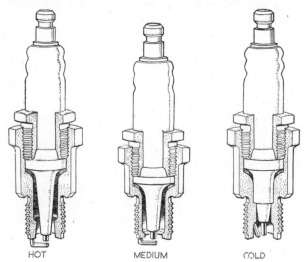

HOT          MEDIUM          COLD

*Fig. 6.13. The longer the centre electrode, the hotter the plug tip. The plugs shown are detachable, i.e. the plug can be dismantled for cleaning*

part of the insulator is highly glazed to prevent electrical leakage due to moisture penetration.

The type of plug illustrated in Fig. 6.12 is described as non-detachable owing to the fact that the central electrode and insulator cannot be removed from the main body. The detachable type of plug, illustrated in Fig. 6.13, is becoming less common. This type of plug can be taken apart for cleaning by unscrewing the top nut. Non-detachable plugs,

77

however, can be cleaned quite satisfactorily on sand-blasting machines available at most garages.

Although the screw thread of the sparking plug is in contact with the water-cooled cylinder head, the plug electrodes reach a very much higher temperature. Different plugs are designed to run at higher or lower temperatures to suit the requirements of different engines. A "cold" plug used in a worn engine which consumes a lot of oil will become fouled with oil and should be replaced by a "hot" plug. If, however, a "hot" plug is used in an engine subjected to much hard driving there is a danger of pre-ignition—the tip of the plug may become sufficiently hot to ignite the mixture before the passage of the spark. The running temperature of the plug is largely determined by the distance of the tip of the centre electrode from the colder body which supports it. Hot and cold versions of the same basic sparking plug are shown in Fig. 6.13.

The gap setting between the electrodes varies from ·018 to ·035 in. according to the particular make of engine. The gap and plug specified by the manufacturer should be adhered to, since the ignition equipment will have been designed on this basis. To obtain the best engine performance and economy, the plugs should be removed every 3,000 miles or so for cleaning and re-setting of the gaps by bending the outer electrodes.

### Magneto Ignition

Although the magneto was once the basis of most motor-car ignition systems, it has now been almost entirely superseded by the coil ignition system already described. Nevertheless, the two systems are very similar in principle. Each uses the principle of inducing a high voltage in a secondary winding by interrupting the current in a primary winding. In both systems, the two coils are wound on a common iron core and the contact breaker is mechanically driven. The chief difference is that, whereas a coil ignition system obtains its operating current from the battery, the magneto generates its own electricity supply. This can be done either by rotating the coil between the poles of a permanent magnet or by rotating a permanent magnet in the vicinity of the stationary coil.

Since a magneto has to generate its own current, it is not very effective at low speed. For starting, therefore, the battery-coil ignition system is more effective. At high engine speeds, however, the performance of a magneto surpasses that of coil ignition and magnetos are therefore more suited to racing and sports cars than to the average private car.

### Suppression of Radio Interference

The electrical discharge at the sparking plugs produces interference which can be picked up on radio and television receivers. To people living in a busy neighbourhood this radio interference can be a considerable nuisance and it is only fair that motorists and manufacturers should reduce the interference by fitting suppressors. Suppressors are a legal requirement on modern cars and whilst cars fitted with them may still give rise to some interference, they are unlikely to be serious offenders.

The simplest form of suppressor consists of an electrical resistor fitted in the high-tension lead from the coil. Its effect is to limit the interference without detriment to the ignition. The same effect can be produced by giving a high resistance to the carbon brush which connects the high-tension coil lead to the rotor arm. A separate suppressor, if required, is easily fitted and costs only a few shillings.

# Chapter 7

# THE PETROL SUPPLY

IN previous chapters the provision of a suitable petrol supply to the engine has been taken somewhat for granted. The present chapter is concerned with the two main aspects of this topic: firstly, how the petrol is conveyed from the filler cap to the carburettor; secondly, the differences in quality that make one petrol more suitable than another for a particular engine. The first aspect leads to a discussion of mechanical and electrical petrol pumps, whilst the second is covered by a discussion of compression ratio, pinking, octane rating, benzole and alcohol.

### From Filler Cap to Float Chamber

A car doing 30 miles to the gallon must carry about 9 gallons of petrol if it is to be able to cover 250 miles between refills. This quantity necessitates a petrol tank equal in volume to a tank 9 in. × 9 in. × 32 in. The actual tank dimensions can be adjusted to suit the vehicle but clearly the petrol tank is bound to be a fairly bulky component and it is not usually convenient to place it near the engine. Moreover, this position would involve considerable fire risk in the event of an accident. Usually the tank is tucked away at the rear of the car not far from the rear axle as shown in Fig. 7.1.

To reach the float chamber which is embodied in the carburettor at the side of the engine, the petrol must be led from the bottom of the tank to the front of the car through a tube. Unfortunately the float chamber is usually at a higher level than the petrol in the tank and it is therefore impossible for petrol to reach the engine from the tank without the assistance of a petrol *pump*. As the difference in level is quite small the pump need only build up a gentle pressure; high pressure would in fact be a disadvantage since it would prevent the float valve from sealing properly. Mechanical pumps, driven from the engine camshaft, are usually employed but electric pumps are also widely used and both types are described below. The petrol pump usually incorporates a filtering gauze to prevent dirt and scale from

80

the tank reaching the carburettor but separate filters may also be used. Without a *petrol gauge* on the instrument panel the driver would frequently be at a loss to know whether he had enough petrol for the journey and how much more the tank would take without overflowing. Strictly speaking the gauge itself is mounted on the petrol tank whilst the instrument on the panel is simply a small ammeter electrically connected to the gauge. The chief parts of the gauge are an electric resistance coil fed with current from the battery and a cork float attached to a lever. The lever is arranged to move a sliding contact along the coil causing the current flowing through the ammeter on the panel to vary.

Although petrol gauges give a useful indication of the petrol contents, they are not usually very accurate, particularly with a shallow form of tank. To protect the driver from running out of petrol a small reserve supply is sometimes available and brought into use when the main tank is empty. A small pipe is fitted to the top of the tank to help air to escape from the tank during filling. The pipe also acts as an overflow to some extent when too much petrol is accidentally supplied; the end of the pipe is turned down so that the petrol spills on to the ground.

The filler cap is often wired to the filler to prevent loss and occasionally it is fitted with a lock. Various attempts have been made to make the

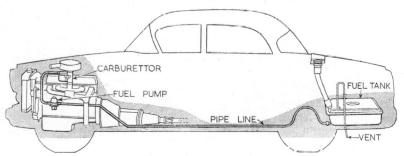

*Fig. 7.1. A small pump is required to make petrol flow upwards from the petrol tank to the carburettor*

filler unobtrusive. Sometimes it is covered with a small removable panel set flush with the body surface whilst one recent car has a combined petrol filler cap and rear reflector (*see* Fig. 7.2).

### Mechanical Petrol Pumps

Most popular cars use a mechanically operated petrol pump (often referred to as a fuel pump) manufactured by A.C. The pump is usually mounted on the side of the crankcase on the same side of the engine as the camshaft by which it is driven. Several designs of pump differing

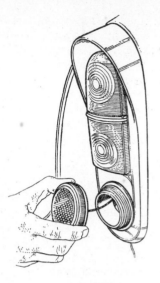

Fig. 7.2. *A combined filler cap and rear reflector*

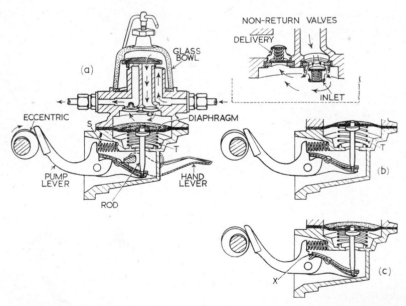

Fig. 7.3. *A mechanically operated A.C. petrol pump. In diagram (a) the pump lever has just caused the diaphragm to move downwards, thus causing petrol from the tank to enter the pump; diagram (b) shows the spring T moving the diaphragm upwards, thus causing delivery of petrol to the float chamber; diagram (c) shows the pump lever " breaking " at X when the diaphragm is prevented from rising by closure of the carburettor float valve*

in points of detail are in use but all of them operate on the same principle which can be described by referring to the design illustrated in Fig. 7.3.

A flexible diaphragm made of petrol-resisting fabric is clamped between the petrol chamber and the lower part of the pump. The engine camshaft is formed with a circular disc on it mounted off-centre and known as an *eccentric* because of its wobbling motion. A lever is pivoted in the lower part of the pump body, one end of it bearing against the eccentric and the other engaging with a vertical rod attached to the centre of the diaphragm. As the eccentric rotates the end of the lever inside the pump body is pushed downwards and this motion is transmitted through the rod to the flexible diaphragm. Suction or a partial vacuum is thus created in the petrol chamber and petrol accordingly flows from the main petrol tank and enters the petrol chamber through the filter gauze and the non-return valve. It is the atmospheric pressure which causes the petrol to flow in response to the suction in the petrol chamber; consequently, it is important that the petrol tank should not be completely sealed (another reason for the vent pipe mentioned in the last section). The non-return valve consists of a light-weight disc held closed by a weak spring except when an excess of pressure on the other side of the disc overcomes the force of the spring. The glass bowl covering the filter gauze makes it possible to see when cleaning is required, by the accumulation of sediment in the filter chamber.

The lever between the eccentric and the diaphragm rod is made in two parts and will only transmit a *pull* to the rod; as the eccentric radius diminishes, the spring S keeps this end of the lever in contact with the eccentric but the other end is free to remain in its downward position. To ensure the upward, that is the delivery, movement of the diaphragm, a second spring T presses against its lower face. It is this spring that causes the delivery of petrol and not the action of the lever; the lever serves for charging the spring during the suction or downward movement of the diaphragm. As the spring pushes the diaphragm upwards, petrol is forced through the second non-return valve and through the delivery pipe to the float chamber. The second valve is, of course, mounted upside down with respect to the first valve.

The force exerted by the spring on the diaphragm is quite small so that the pressure of the petrol delivered is only 2 or 3 pounds per square inch. The buoyancy of the float in the float chamber (*see* p. 51) is sufficient to keep the float valve sealed against the pump pressure when the petrol level in the float chamber is high. If the pump lever were made in one piece so that it could push the diaphragm up as well as pulling it down, the delivery pressure would not be limited; the float valve would be forced open and petrol would flow continuously causing

83

the carburettor to overflow. With the arrangement used, petrol flows intermittently and the amount delivered equals the amount drawn from the carburettor by the engine.

Most mechanical petrol pumps are provided with a hand-operated priming lever. If the engine has been standing idle for a considerable period the carburettor may be empty and a few strokes of the priming lever will help to ensure a quick start and avoid straining the battery.

### Electric Petrol Pumps

Electric petrol pumps have long been employed on sports cars and those of higher price and are now widely used on the less expensive popular cars. One advantage of the electric pump is that it starts operating as soon as the ignition key closes the circuit, so that by the time the engine starter is operated, petrol has been delivered to the

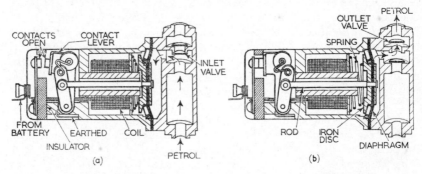

*Fig. 7.4. An electrically operated S.U. petrol pump. (a) shows the end of the suction stroke; the diaphragm has been drawn to the left by pull of the coil and the contacts have just opened. (b) shows petrol being delivered as the spring forces the diaphragm to the right; the contacts have just closed*

float chamber. The pump can be located in any convenient position on the car since it draws its operating current from the battery and is independent of the engine. By mounting the pump far away from the engine, the pump is kept cool and the danger of interruption of the petrol supply due to a vapour-lock is avoided.

The only difference in principle between the mechanical and the electric petrol pump is that, in a mechanical pump, the suction stroke of the diaphragm is caused by an engine-operated lever whilst, in an electric pump, the same stroke is produced by an electromagnet. The principle of the S.U. electric pump can be described by referring to Fig. 7.4 which is somewhat simplified in order to make the operation clearer. Current from the battery is fed to the coil which then behaves as though it were a magnet (this principle has already been referred to in connection with the ignition coil on p. 67). The iron disc attached to the diaphragm is attracted towards the coil and petrol is drawn into the space on the right of the diaphragm through the inlet valve which is lifted off its seat. A bronze rod is attached to the centre of the disc and passes through the centre of the coil. At the end of the stroke, the rod causes the contact lever to swing open, so breaking the circuit. The magnetic force vanishes and the spring forces the diaphragm back to the right thus forcing petrol through the outlet valve whilst the inlet valve drops back on to its seat. Towards the end of the delivery stroke the rod causes the contact lever to spring across in the reverse direction, so closing the contacts and energizing the coil once more. If the float chamber is full and the float valve closed, the diaphragm remains still, since the spring is too weak to overcome the float valve. The action of the pump is therefore very similar to that of the mechanical pump previously described.

## The Production of Petrol

The motor car as we know it depends on the fact that petrol can be readily made to release its store of energy by burning it in a petrol engine. This remarkable liquid is obtained from natural oil found in underground reservoirs in various parts of the world. Natural or crude oil is a thick, dark-coloured liquid which is believed to have been formed many millions of years ago from the decay of marine life. Crude oil is usually found in layers of porous rock and is often under considerable pressure. In such cases, the oil can force its own way to the surface, after a hole has been drilled, without the necessity for pumping. The largest known reserves of oil are in the Middle East but other important oil fields exist in the U.S.A., Mexico, Venezuela, the East Indies and elsewhere. Because of the great importance of oil to industry, continuous prospecting for new fields is going ahead all over the world.

Petrol consists of the more volatile elements in crude oil—those which boil below a temperature of 400°F—and is obtained by the distillation of crude oil in a refinery. A typical crude oil yields about 25 per cent of its weight in petrol by this process. Further petrol can be obtained from the less volatile residue by a process known as " cracking " which consists of breaking heavy molecules into lighter ones. The introduction of this process in modern refineries has greatly increased our petrol supplies.

## Compression Ratio and Pinking

It is well known that the performance of an engine can be improved by increasing the compression ratio and in recent years compression ratios have been rising steadily. The meaning of the term " compression

85

ratio " is illustrated in Fig. 7.5. It is the ratio of the volume enclosed by the piston at the bottom of its stroke to the volume enclosed at the top of its stroke. The compression ratio of an existing engine can be increased quite simply in two ways as illustrated in Fig. 7.6. One

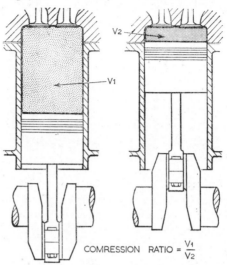

$$\text{COMPRESSION RATIO} = \frac{V_1}{V_2}$$

*Fig. 7.5. Compression Ratio is the volume enclosed by the piston at the bottom of its stroke divided by the volume enclosed at the top of its stroke*

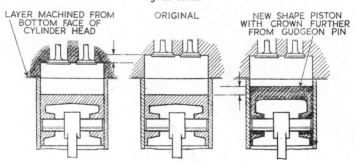

*Fig. 7.6. Two methods of raising the compression ratio*

is to remove a layer of metal from the face of the cylinder head, thus reducing the enclosed volume when the piston is at top dead centre. (A similar effect can sometimes be achieved by using a thinner cylinder-head gasket.) The second method is to use a piston having a greater distance between the crown and gudgeon pin. Both these methods are occasionally used for improving the engine of a new model without introducing expensive design modifications but eventually it becomes necessary to modify the general design to obtain further improvement.

The extent to which the performance of an engine can be improved by raising the compression ratio is, however, strictly limited by the tendency of all petrols towards "knocking" or "pinking". These names describe the hard, metallic noise which is sometimes heard when an engine is labouring at wide throttle and low speed. Pinking is symptomatic of a violent type of combustion which occurs when a portion of the mixture away from the sparking plug explodes when at high pressure and temperature. Normally the flame spreads smoothly from the sparking plug throughout the cylinder, but at high compression ratio, some of the charge may become overheated and compressed by the advancing flame and "detonation" occurs (*see* Fig. 7.7). Provided it

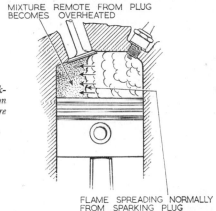

MIXTURE REMOTE FROM PLUG
BECOMES OVERHEATED

*Fig. 7.7. "Pinking" or "Knocking" is due to the sudden combustion of an overheated portion of the mixture remote from the sparking plug*

FLAME SPREADING NORMALLY
FROM SPARKING PLUG

does not occur continuously, pinking is not particularly harmful to an engine. Persistent pinking, however, leads to increased wear and the scouring action of the explosion wave causes overheating. This, in turn, may give rise to another trouble known as "pre-ignition"; a small deposit on some part of the combustion chamber reaches glow heat and causes the mixture to ignite before the spark has occurred. It is this effect that sometimes causes a hot engine to continue running after the ignition has been switched off. Pre-ignition leads to loss of power and to further overheating and can be very harmful if allowed to continue.

If an engine is run at fixed speed and at full throttle on a standard grade petrol and is tested in increasing compression ratios, it is found that pinking becomes noticeable at a certain compression ratio; beyond that, the performance ceases to improve and, in fact, becomes worse

(Fig. 7.8). " Premium " and " super premium " petrols are now available which have greater resistance to knock; by running on these petrols, the compression ratio can be increased still further and the gain in performance before pinking occurs is appreciable. The best petrol for a particular engine depends on its compression ratio. Older cars having compression ratios of only 5 or 6 to 1 run perfectly well on standard grade petrol; use of premium grades would only be a waste of money. Current makes of popular cars having compression ratios up

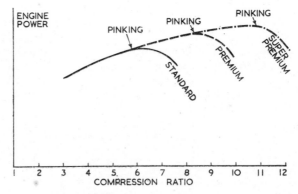

*Fig. 7.8. Power increases as compression ratio is raised up to the point where pinking becomes serious*

to 8½ to 1 require premium petrol in order to avoid pinking and get the best performance. (Pinking is not always a sign that a higher grade of petrol is needed; it is sometimes due to the ignition being unnecessarily far advanced.) At present few cars, apart from some high compression ratio sports cars, would benefit from using super premium petrol, but as engine designers are continuing to push up compression ratios generally, super premium petrol may soon become a necessity. Engine design and fuel technology are interdependent.

### Octane Rating

The ability of a petrol to resist knocking is assessed by means of a system known as octane rating. The petrol under test is compared with a blend of two reference fuels, one of which, heptane, has a very poor resistance to knock whilst the other, iso-octane, has very good resistance. A special test engine, designed so that its compression ratio can be varied whilst running, is run on the petrol under test and the compression ratio at which knocking occurs is observed. The same engine is then run on various blends of heptane and iso-octane and the blend giving rise to knock at the same compression ratio as the petrol under test is thus determined. If the equivalent blend contains 70 per cent iso-octane, the petrol tested is said to have an octane number of 70. A 100 octane petrol is one having the same knock resistance as pure iso-octane; super premium petrols are in this class.

Most petrols have certain substances added to them in small quantities in order to improve their knock resistance, the most important being tetra-ethyl lead. Further petrol additives are also used to reduce cylinder deposits and prevent corrosion and pre-ignition.

### Benzole and Alcohol

Benzole, like petrol, is a compound of carbon and hydrogen but is derived from coal during the manufacture of coke and coal gas. Its octane rating is good and it contains rather more energy to the gallon than petrol. The supply, however, is limited and it is usually blended with lower grades of petrol to improve their performance.

Unlike petrol and benzole, alcohol contains oxygen in combination with carbon and hydrogen. It is not surprising, therefore, that alcohol contains considerably less energy to the gallon than the others since the oxygen itself cannot burn. Alcohol does not occur naturally but is manufactured mainly from vegetable matter; it is usually sold blended with petrol. Its chief advantage as a fuel for petrol engines lies in the large quantity of heat it absorbs during vaporization. Cooling the charge causes it to shrink and enables the engine to consume a greater quantity. The increase in power so obtained makes alcohol a particularly suitable fuel for racing engines.

Chapter 8

# ENGINE LUBRICATION

I T is common knowledge that lubrication makes things run more easily whether they are lawn mowers or bicycles. Not only is less effort required to operate them, but the wear of the moving parts is greatly reduced and the machines last longer. The amount of power exerted on a lawn mower is quite small, of course, and the speed of the moving parts is low. If, as often happens, the busy gardener forgets all about lubrication until reminded of it by squeaks from the suffering mower, no great harm is done. A similar carefree attitude applied to the engine of a motor car, however, could easily result in very serious damage to the engine. Lubrication is not just a useful way of making the engine run easily and reducing its rate of wear. Without lubrication, the engine would not run at all.

### Why Engine Lubrication is Vital

When one metal surface slides over another, work has to be done in overcoming friction and this work is converted into heat. This frictional loss depends on the pressure between the two surfaces and when, as in a petrol engine, the pressure is large, the loss is correspondingly great. The most important sliding surfaces in an engine are those in the crankshaft bearings and those between the cylinder walls and the pistons and piston rings. The pressure acting in the crankshaft bearings is very high owing to the gas pressure on the pistons and the forces due to inertia of the moving parts at high speed. The side thrust on the pistons due to the connecting rods and the pressure exerted on the cylinder walls by the piston rings are also considerable. However smoothly these running surfaces were machined, the power absorbed by friction when running at high speed without lubrication would be tremendous. Very high temperatures would be developed between the moving surfaces and one surface would tend to pick up metal from the other causing even greater friction. In a second or two, the surfaces would become locked together or " seized ". Even supposing an engine could run without lubrication and escape mechanical harm, the power absorbed by friction would probably rival that developed by the combustion gases and the amount left over for propelling the car would be very small. By ensuring the continual presence of a thin film of oil between all moving surfaces, the whole picture is completely changed. The power absorbed by friction may be reduced to around 10 per cent of the total and the rate of wear is so greatly reduced that the engine may cover 50,000 miles or more before any part needs replacement. Far from seizing in a few seconds, the crankshaft may have turned some 200 million times and the engine should still be fully serviceable.

### Pressure Lubrication

A simple but rather crude way of lubricating an engine would be to fill the sump with oil to a certain level and then to rely upon the extremities of the moving crankshaft to splash oil into the right places. The reliability and long life of the modern engine has, however, been

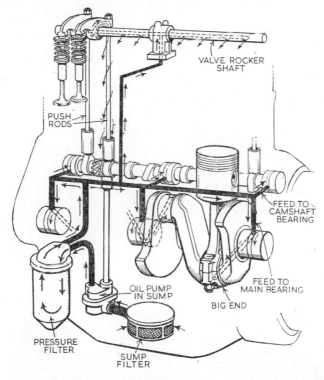

*Fig.* 8.1. *Lubrication system for a 4-cylinder, overhead valve engine. A small pump draws oil from the sump and feeds it under pressure to the crankshaft, the camshaft and the overhead valve gear*

achieved by the adoption of pressure lubrication. Oil is still stored in the sump but a small oil pump is used to pump oil under pressure to all the important running surfaces. On the overhead-valve engine lubrication system illustrated in Fig. 8.1, oil is fed under pressure to the following parts: the crankshaft main bearings; the big-end bearings; the camshaft; the rocker bearings in the overhead-valve gear; and the cups in the ends of the pushrods beneath the tappet adjusting screws.

It would, of course, be possible to distribute oil from the pump through a network of pipes but nowadays, whenever possible, the oil is

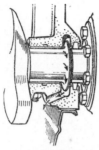

*Fig. 8.2. An oil " thrower ring " behind the crankshaft rear bearing is used to prevent oil from leaking into the clutch housing*

fed through channels drilled in the engine parts themselves. This method is more reliable as there is less danger of oil failure due to leaks or broken pipes. The oil pump is partially submerged in the sump below the crankshaft and is driven from the camshaft; often the drive is combined with that of the distributor as mentioned earlier (*see* Fig. 6.7). After passing through the main filter, the oil enters a main gallery running the length of the cylinder block which feeds the three main crankshaft bearings. Oil is fed to the camshaft bearings through passages from the crankshaft main bearings. Pressurized oil may also be fed to the valve tappets through passages drilled in the cylinder block. Oil for the timing chain and wheels can be tapped from the camshaft front bearing. The details of the oil distribution system vary from one engine to another but many of the main features of the system described here are common to all popular overhead-valve engines.

To prevent oil from the rear main bearing from escaping into the clutch housing, it is usual to form a " thrower ring " on the crankshaft as shown in Fig. 8.2. If oil creeps along the shaft, it is flung off when it reaches the ring and drains back to the sump through the hole provided. Another thrower ring is often fitted to the front of the crankshaft to prevent oil from escaping through the timing-chain cover. This ring is made detachable to allow the timing-chain sprocket to be slid on to the shaft.

As the big-end bearings are in motion, their oil supply has to be carried through the crankshaft itself (Fig. 8.3). Passages are drilled in the crankshaft between the main journals and the crankpins. On the engine shown, a hole in the big end of the connecting rod coincides intermittently with the hole in the crankshaft so that a series of small squirts of oil are directed on to the cylinder walls. In many engines, cylinder wall lubrication is entirely due to oil mist and the splash of oil flung out from the bearings. The sliding speed of the bearing surfaces in the small end of the connecting rod is comparatively low and pressure lubrication is usually considered unnecessary. Sometimes, however, the gudgeon pins may be pressure-lubricated through passages in the connecting rod.

Oil distribution to the valve rocker arms is achieved by using the hollow rocker shaft as an oil gallery. The oil supply to the valve gear is usually restricted by placing a small orifice in the main feed. Excessive delivery to the head may result in heavy oil consumption and smoky exhaust due to oil finding its way into the manifolds through the valve guides. A drain passage leading through the cylinder head and block

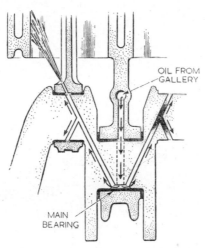

*Fig. 8.9. Oil for the big ends is obtained from the main bearings through passages drilled in the crankshaft. Oil is sometimes directed on to the cylinder walls through a small hole in the connecting-rod big end*

to the sump, is provided not only as a return for oil escaping from the overhead-valve gear, but also as a channel for adding fresh oil to the sump through the filler cap in the valve cover.

When the engine is running, some of the hot gases are bound to leak past the pistons into the crankcase. If the crankcase were completely

Fig. 8.4. A gear-type oil pump. One gear wheel is directly driven from the camshaft; the other is an idler

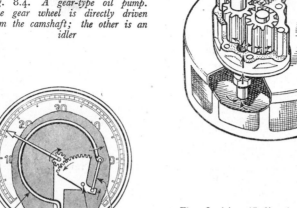

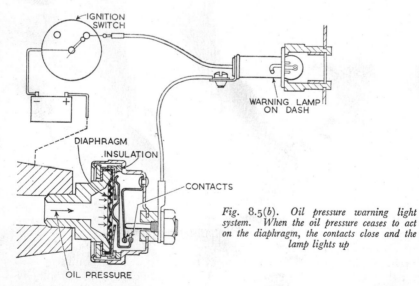

FLEXIBLE TUBE

LINK

PIVOT

AIR

CONNECTION TO OIL SYSTEM

Fig. 8.5(a). (Left) An oil pressure gauge. The pressure from the oil tends to unwind the flexible tube, causing the needle to rotate

IGNITION SWITCH

WARNING LAMP ON DASH

DIAPHRAGM

INSULATION

CONTACTS

Fig. 8.5(b). Oil pressure warning light system. When the oil pressure ceases to act on the diaphragm, the contacts close and the lamp lights up

OIL PRESSURE

94

air-tight, the pressure would build up and might give rise to trouble. The engine illustrated in Fig. 3.2 has an air vent or breather fitted to the side of the tappet chamber which communicates with the crankcase. In addition, a rubber tube is sometimes fitted between the valve cover and air cleaner, so that fumes are drawn into the engine and all the oil spaces of the engine are kept ventilated.

Part of the function of lubrication is to remove heat from bearings and rubbing surfaces. It is therefore necessary for the oil to be able to dispose of this heat otherwise the oil would become overheated and fail to act effectively as a lubricant and coolant. Some high-performance engines are fitted with an oil cooler which functions in the same way as the main radiator. On most engines, however, the heat is dissipated through the walls of the sump, sometimes with the aid of cooling fins.

### The Oil Pump and Oil-pressure Control

The type of oil pump used on most modern engines is a gear pump which consists basically of two small gear-wheels (Fig. 8.4). One wheel is mounted on the main spindle which is driven from the engine camshaft, whilst the other wheel meshes with the first and is rotated by it. The pump draws its oil supply from the sump through a wire gauze filter; sometimes the filter is arranged to float on the oil surface in order to prevent the entry of sludge from the bottom of the sump. Apart from leakage, oil does not flow between the meshing teeth but is carried round to the delivery side of the pump by the outer teeth of both wheels. The required delivery pressure is usually in the range of 30–60 lb/in². The speed of the pump, however, depends on the speed of the engine and, unless some form of pressure control is used, excessive pressure would be developed at high engine speed; this would lead to unnecessary power absorption and overheating of the oil. A pressure relief valve is therefore provided between the pump delivery and the main oil channel. The valve may be a separate component or it may be incorporated in the pump. When the oil pressure exceeds a predetermined value, a spring-loaded plunger is forced back uncovering a port so that oil is returned to the sump.

A failure in the oil supply can soon result in serious damage to the engine and some form of oil-pressure indicator is required on the instrument panel. The best type of indicator is undoubtedly a dial pressure gauge with a needle showing the actual oil pressure in the main gallery (Fig. 8.5(a)). The pressure of the oil causes the coiled tube to unwind so turning the indicator needle. In recent years, however, more and more cars have only been fitted with an oil warning light, the main justification for this cost-saving expedient being the normal reliability of modern lubrication systems. The light is controlled by a pressure-operated switch which is held open so long as the oil pressure exceeds the safe value. If the pressure falls below this value, the switch closes and the warning lamp lights up on the panel (Fig. 8.5(b)).

The lamp system is all or nothing. A dial gauge, on the other hand, gives a continuous reading of oil pressure. When the engine is started from cold, the oil is thick and difficult to pump so the gauge may first register a high pressure and fall back gradually as the engine warms up; this behaviour is quite normal.

Neither of these systems provides a sure guarantee that all is well with the lubrication. If the oil passage to a particular bearing becomes blocked, the flow to the bearing may be interrupted whilst the oil pressure remains high. In such a case, the warning light system would not respond in any way, whilst the increased pressure shown by a dial gauge would be too small for even the most observant driver to notice.

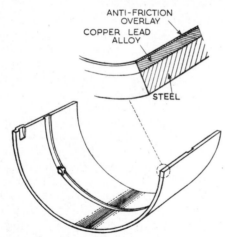

Fig. 8.6. *A modern steel shell half bearing, with a copper lead lining to withstand high bearing pressure, and a thin soft metal overlay to reduce friction*

However, with modern oils and oil filters, troubles of this kind are rare. In the more likely event of complete failure in the oil supply due to a leak in the pressure system or neglect of the oil level in the sump, both systems provide adequate warning.

### Big-end and Main Bearings

The use of split bearing shells for the big-end and main bearings has already been mentioned in Chapter 3 and a bearing of this type is shown in Fig. 3.6. At one time thick shells of white metal were either inserted or cast directly inside the cast-iron main bearings and the steel big-ends. The friction of a steel or cast-iron crankshaft running in oil-lubricated bearings of white metal is very low and the rate of wear on the crankshaft is small. White metal, however, contains a high proportion of tin and is expensive; it is also a comparatively soft metal and is liable to become crushed and distorted if the lining is too thick and the bearing load is high. Also the refitting of a worn bearing of this type is somewhat costly.

Modern practice is to line the main bearings and big-ends with thin cylindrical steel shells made in two halves. The inner surfaces of the shells are lined with a soft bearing material such as white metal. Steel-backed bearings wear well and will stand higher loading than thick plain white-metal linings. Steel shell bearings are mass produced in a great variety of sizes and when a bearing becomes worn it can easily be replaced (Fig. 8.6).

In recent years, bearing loads have been increasing rapidly due to the use of higher compression ratios. Some engines therefore use steel shells lined with an alloy of copper and lead for the big-end bearings where the loading is particularly severe. Copper-lead linings will withstand considerably greater loads than white metal but they give rise to rather more friction. To overcome this difficulty, the main lining is faced with an extremely thin layer of some special anti-friction material such as lead.

### Cylinder-wall Lubrication and Piston Rings

If the petrol engine did not exist and an inventor were to come along and propose the idea, it is quite possible that an engineer examining the proposal would reply in this vein: " I grant that you might be able to make your mixture of petrol and air ignite at the right instant and burn quickly enough to repeat the process hundreds of times a minute; but how can you possibly have a piston in contact with burning gases and rushing up and down inside a cylinder without the thing wearing out in five minutes?" If the inventor were to claim that the engine would run for 50,000 miles or more with only a few thousandths of an inch wear in the cylinder bore, the engineer would probably decide that the fellow was quite mad or, at best, somewhat unrealistic. Yet the rate of wear in a modern engine lubricated with a high-grade oil is of this order.

There is a twofold explanation for this remarkable phenomenon. Firstly, the piston is not in contact with the cylinder wall as it rushes up and down but is separated from it by a film of lubricating oil. The piston rings, which take up the clearance between the piston and cylinder and prevent the leakage of hot gases past the piston, might be expected to wear rapidly but they too are seldom in direct contact with the wall. As they slide up and down they ride on a thin film of oil. It might be thought that the oil film would be squeezed out by the spring pressure exerted by the rings on the cylinder walls (the rings have to be com-pressed into their grooves before a piston can be inserted in its cylinder).

97

It is, however, a fact that when a ring slides rapidly in a cylinder, sufficient pressure builds up in the oil film to hold the ring off the wall. When the piston is not in motion, the ring expands again and makes contact with the wall. It is not surprising, therefore, to find that the cylinder bore becomes most badly worn at the top and bottom of the stroke where the piston velocity reaches zero; also that wear of piston rings and cylinder walls is high when the engine is made to labour at low speed in top gear.

The second part of the explanation lies in the fact that the cylinder walls are cooled. Heat from the piston is transferred through the rings

*Fig. 8.7. A typical engine piston with the oil scraper ring and the upper of the three compression rings removed*

and oil film to the cylinder walls from which it is carried away by the continuous circulation of either water or air. In this way the piston is prevented from becoming overheated.

The type of piston ring most commonly used consists of a plain ring of cast iron with a small cut in it so that the ring can be opened sufficiently to slip it over the crown of the piston; the ring is rectangular in cross-section (Fig. 8.7). It may seem surprising that rings should be made of cast iron but this metal wears extremely well, develops a high polish and can be produced in the springy form required. Usually two or three identical rings are used in the upper grooves but it is becoming increasingly common for the rubbing surface of the top ring to be chromium plated; the top ring is exposed to the full gas pressure and the chrome finish prolongs its life considerably. More elaborate forms of ring have been designed to give more complete sealing against " blow-by " of the hot gases and improved lubrication but it is very difficult to make reliable comparisons.

Oil is delivered to the cylinder wall by splash and other means. The thickness of the oil film required for good lubrication is very small and it is necessary to remove the excess oil in order to restrict the amount of oil getting past the piston rings. If too much oil is left on the cylinder wall as the piston descends during the firing stroke, much of it will be burnt and the oil consumption will be high. The bottom ring is therefore designed to remove excess oil from the walls and return it to the sump. The " scraper " ring shown in Fig. 8.7 is slotted and holes are drilled in the piston groove for draining away the excess oil. Sometimes the scraper ring has no slots and the piston holes are placed below the ring; as the piston descends, the excess oil builds up beneath the scraper and drains away through the piston holes.

## Oil Filtration

Although a wire-gauze filter is normally fitted on the oil-pump inlet in the sump, this would be quite useless in protecting the bearing surfaces from the smaller abrasive particles that find their way into the oil. These particles may consist of dust and grit that have got past the air filter or have entered through the crankcase breather; they may be from hard deposits that build up in the cylinder; or perhaps they are metallic particles left behind in one of the oil-passage drillings during manufacture. The life of the engine is considerably prolonged by

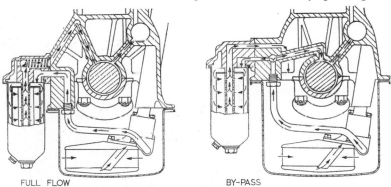

FULL FLOW             BY-PASS

*Fig. 8.8. With full-flow oil filtration, all the oil from the pump passes through the filter. With by-pass filtration, the oil is cleaned by passing part of the pump delivery through the filter and then returning it to the sump*

fitting a special oil filter for removing particles from the oil and this is universal practice nowadays.

The filtering element is usually made either of felt or of a special type of impregnated paper. In order that the filter shall not offer too much resistance to the flow, the surface area of the element must be fairly large and this is usually achieved by pleating the element.

The oil circulation through the filter can be arranged in two ways. Either the whole of the oil supply from the pump can be made to pass through the filter giving " full flow " filtration; this is the method used on the system shown in Fig. 8.1. Alternatively, the bulk of the oil supply can be delivered direct to the main oil system whilst the remainder is passed through a " by-pass " filter and returned to the sump (Fig. 8.8). Clearly the full-flow system is more effective since oil cannot reach a bearing from the sump without passing through the filter; in the by-pass system, a particle in the oil can circulate through the bearings several times before it happens to be trapped in the filter. The advantage of the by-pass filter, of course, is that it only has to pass

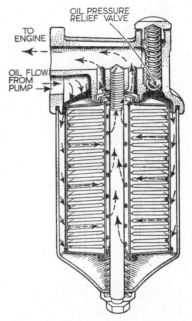

*Fig. 8.9. A full-flow oil filter with a pressure relief valve which opens when the pressure drop becomes excessive due to clogging of the filter surfaces*

part of the pump delivery and it is therefore smaller and cheaper; nevertheless, the modern trend is towards full flow.

Whichever type of filter is used, it must be placed on the pressure side of the pump to avoid restricting the flow into the pump. The filter case has therefore to withstand the full oil pressure and must be fairly substantial. A typical full-flow filter, for mounting on the side of the crankcase, is shown in Fig. 8.9. The filter element is supported in a perforated metal cage and is renewed every 7,000 miles or so when it is becoming clogged. If the filter were to become blocked, the oil supply to the bearings would be interrupted; to guard against this possibility, a relief valve is incorporated and arranged to open when the filter resistance becomes excessive.

## Some Notes about Oil

By a strange coincidence, the best lubricants for motor vehicle engines are various grades of oil obtained from the same source as petrol, that is, from crude oil. The proportion of lubricating oil obtained from crude oil is small compared with that of petrol, but this is convenient since the lubricating oil consumption of all engines is very small compared with their fuel consumption. We speak of petrol consumption in terms of 20, 30 or 40 miles to the gallon but oil consumption is often reckoned in terms of several hundreds of miles to the pint.

A good engine oil has to satisfy several different requirements. It should be fairly thin when cold for ease of starting, but it must not become too thin when hot, otherwise the oil films in the bearings and between the piston rings and cylinder walls may break down. It must have a tendency to cling to metal surfaces so that the various parts are protected from corrosion when the engine is idle and lubricated from the outset when the engine is started. Furthermore, the oil should have a long life and not tend to form acids or sludge by decomposing.

Various systems have been devised for classifying motor oils. It is impossible for a simple grade number to express all the different properties required and oils are usually classified according to a single but particularly important property, their viscosity. Oil viscosity is a measure of the resistance to sliding of two surfaces separated by a film of the oil in question. A low-viscosity oil will therefore reduce the power lost in engine friction. Unfortunately, the lower the viscosity, the greater is the tendency for the oil film to break down under pressure, so there is a limit beyond which it would be unsafe to use a thinner oil. The system devised by the American Society of Automotive Engineers (S.A.E.) is to assign a number to an oil whose viscosity lies in a certain range. Since viscosity varies considerably with temperature, a particular temperature, usually 210°F, is specified. An oil graded as S.A.E.20, for instance, has its viscosity within a specified range at 210°F. The lower the S.A.E. number, the thinner the oil. Thus an oil graded as S.A.E.30 is suitable for summer use in Britain whilst the thinner grade S.A.E.20 would be more suitable in the winter. If an engine has to operate in a cold climate, the viscosity of the oil at very low temperature is also important. The S.A.E. system meets this point by having a second series of gradings determined at 0°F and distinguished by the addition of the letter W.

Oils obtained by the straightforward refinement and purification of crude oil are known as " straight " mineral oils. Since the war, the lubricating properties of straight oils have been greatly improved by the use of " additives "—substances added to the oil. One type of additive makes the oil " detergent " with the result that sticky deposits are prevented from forming on the oiled surfaces. Detergent oils are particularly helpful in preventing the piston rings from sticking in their grooves and in keeping the running parts clean. The dirt, of course, remains suspended in the oil and it is therefore important that the oil should be changed at regular intervals.

Another type of additive can be used to prevent the oil from becoming too thin at 210°F without making it too thick at 0°F. The oil may then fall within two S.A.E. grades and be given a double grading such as S.A.E. 10W/30. Oils of this type are called " multigrade " and are extremely useful in that they combine ease of starting in cold weather with adequate engine protection in hot. The same oil can therefore be used all the year round and petrol consumption is usually reduced more than enough to justify the extra cost of the oil.

# Chapter 9

# ENGINE COOLING

THE heat removed in cooling the cylinder walls and cylinder head of an engine accounts for some 30 per cent of the energy of the petrol. If we could avoid the necessity for cooling, it would be possible to increase the number of miles per gallon by extracting more power and less heat from the combustion gases. Without cooling, however, the lubricating oil would become burnt and the pistons would seize; the valves would wear rapidly due to overheating; and the density of the charge inhaled during the suction stroke would be reduced with a corresponding loss of power. Some form of cooling, then, is an essential feature of all petrol engines (it is interesting to note that the gas turbine, which is free from pistons and valves, does not require cooling; see Chapter 15). The present chapter is devoted to a discussion of engine cooling and associated topics.

## The Two Methods of Cooling

The heat removed from an engine can only be disposed of by passing it into the atmosphere. The simplest method of cooling is therefore the obvious one of passing the heat directly to the atmosphere. Although this method is used almost universally on motor cycles it is far less popular on motor cars. Air is not a very good conductor of heat and it is necessary to increase the area of the cooling surface by forming fins on the cylinder barrels and the cylinder head (see Fig. 9.1(a) ). Since the engine of a motor cycle is well exposed, the natural draught of air gives adequate cooling even when the machine is stationary. Occasionally motor-cycle engines are adapted for small motor cars and with the engine at the front of the vehicle, natural draught is sufficient. On a Volkswagen, however, with a four-cylinder air-cooled engine installed at the rear, a specially designed fan, belt-driven from the crankshaft, is required to give adequate cooling (see Fig. 9.2). The air is directed on to the hot parts of the engine by means of cowling.

The second and more elaborate method of cooling is to incorporate a system of passages in the cylinder block and head and to arrange for the circulation of a liquid coolant, usually water. Water is a very much better conductor of heat than air, and this form of cooling is far more popular among designers. Having transferred the heat from the engine to the water, it is necessary for the water itself to be cooled and this is achieved by passing it through a radiator from which heat is transferred to the atmosphere (Fig. 9.1(b) ). Owing to their solid construction, water-cooled engines tend to be quieter in operation than the air-cooled type.

### The Radiator

At one time the radiator was boldly exposed at the front of the car and its design often assumed a traditional form for a particular make of car. Nowadays the radiator is inside the bonnet and is almost completely concealed by the grille (Fig. 9.3). Sometimes a link with the

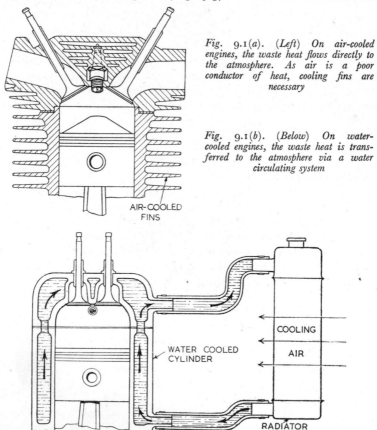

Fig. 9.1(a). (*Left*) *On air-cooled engines, the waste heat flows directly to the atmosphere. As air is a poor conductor of heat, cooling fins are necessary*

Fig. 9.1(b). (*Below*) *On water-cooled engines, the waste heat is transferred to the atmosphere via a water circulating system*

AIR-COOLED FINS

COOLING

WATER COOLED CYLINDER

AIR

RADIATOR

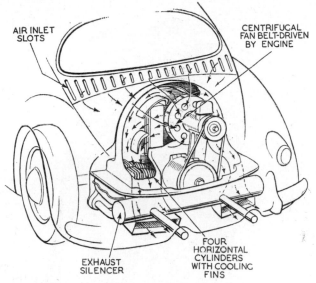

AIR INLET
SLOTS

CENTRIFUGAL
FAN BELT-DRIVEN
BY ENGINE

FOUR
HORIZONTAL
CYLINDERS
WITH COOLING
FINS

EXHAUST
SILENCER

Fig. 9.2. *The Volkswagen has an air-cooled engine installed at the rear. An engine-driven fan draws air through slots in the body and blows it over the engine*

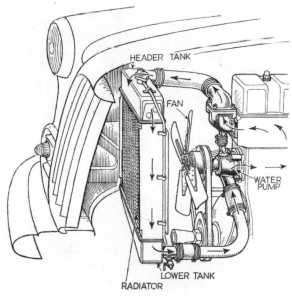

HEADER TANK

FAN

WATER
PUMP

RADIATOR

LOWER TANK

Fig. 9.3. *The radiator of the modern car is tucked away behind the front grille*

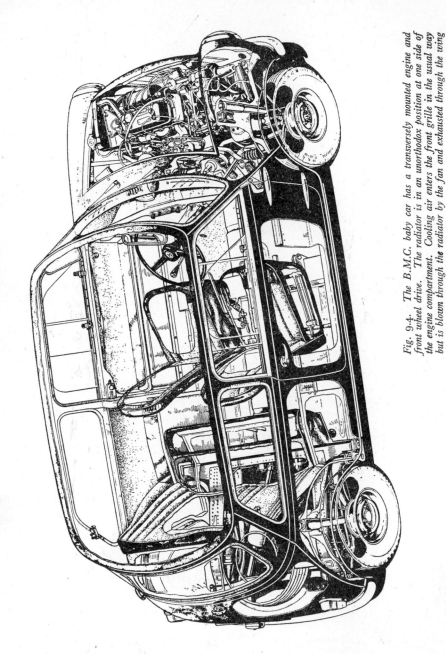

Fig. 9.4. The B.M.C. baby car has a transversely mounted engine and front wheel drive. The radiator is in an unorthodox position at one side of the engine compartment. Cooling air enters the front grille in the usual way but is blown through the radiator by the fan and exhausted through the wing

past is retained by styling the top front of the bonnet in a manner reminiscent of the old radiator design. Engines are normally mounted flexibly to prevent the transmission of engine noise and vibration to the body. The radiator, on the other hand, is fairly rigidly mounted and it is therefore necessary for flexible hose to be used for the connections between the radiator and engine. On the B.M.C. baby car with its transversely mounted engine, the radiator is placed on one side of the engine compartment (Fig. 9.4).

Many different designs of cooling surface have been used in radiators but the general principle is always to provide more surface area on the air side than on the water side (air being a poorer conductor of heat than water). One popular design of radiator employs a few rows of flattish, vertical tubes to which is attached a large number of thin horizontal sheets or fins (Fig. 9.5). The joints between the tubes and fins are soldered to provide an easy path for the flow of heat from the tube to the fin.

### The Fan

When the car is moving at 30 m.p.h. or so, the natural flow of air through the radiator would be quite sufficient in many cases to produce the required dissipation of heat. Unfortunately, however, the designer has also to ensure sufficient cooling when the car is crawling in heavy traffic or toiling up a steep hill at low speed. It is therefore almost universal practice for a fan to be mounted on the front of the engine just behind the radiator (Fig. 9.3). The fan is driven from a pulley on the engine crankshaft through a rubber belt of V-shaped cross-section, the same belt usually driving the dynamo. Above 30 m.p.h. or so, the fan is not required and simply absorbs engine power unnecessarily. It would, of course, be possible to arrange for the fan to cut out when the water temperature fell below a certain value, the only difficulty being the extra cost of a suitable device.

### The Water Pump

The diagram in Fig. 9.1(b) shows the circulation of water taking place naturally according to the principle used in domestic central-heating systems. The water in the radiator is cooler and therefore slightly heavier than the water in the cylinder and flow takes place in the direction shown. This method of water circulation is referred to as the thermo-syphon system. The water flow with this system is rather sluggish and it is necessary to provide large passages in both the engine and the radiator in order not to impede the flow. Nowadays, the more usual practice is to incorporate a small water pump in the engine. The pump consists of a rotating disc or impeller with a few small vanes

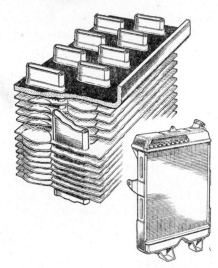

Fig. 9.5. A tube-and-fin radiator. As with air-cooled engines, fins are necessary to overcome the poor heat-conducting properties of air

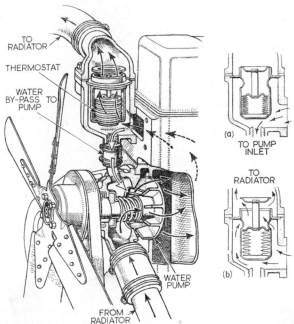

TO RADIATOR

THERMOSTAT

WATER BY-PASS TO PUMP

(a)

TO PUMP INLET

TO RADIATOR

(b)

WATER PUMP

FROM RADIATOR

Fig. 9.6. An engine-driven water pump delivering water to the radiator through an automatic thermostat. When the engine is cold, the thermostat valve is closed and no water flows through the radiator. When the engine becomes hot, the pressure of the vapour in the thermostat bellows causes the valve to open

attached to one side. The pump is usually mounted on the same shaft as the fan and is often housed in the cylinder block just behind the fan (Fig. 9.6). Water enters the " eye " of the impeller flowing parallel to the shaft and is flung out radially between the vanes. The rate of circulation is much greater than with natural circulation and the engine can be designed both for compactness and high output without danger of overheating. The pump usually draws water from the bottom of the radiator and forces it through the cylinder-block water jacket and cylinder-head water passages back to the top of the radiator; the direction of flow is therefore the same as with natural circulation. The water holes in the top of the cylinder block are, of course, arranged to match up with those in the cylinder head and the intervening jointing layer

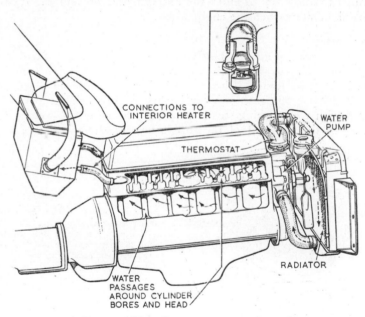

*Fig. 9.7. Water flow passages on a modern engine*

or gasket. A faulty cylinder head joint gives rise not only to gas leakage but to water leakage as well (Fig. 9.7).

### Use of a Pressure Cap

At one time the top of the radiator was always vented to the atmosphere. At normal sea-level atmospheric pressure, water boils at 212°F. If the water temperature reached this value, boiling occurred and water and steam escaped through the vent. In recent years it has become increasingly common for the radiator to be sealed by a pressure cap which incorporates a spring-loaded valve (Fig. 9.8). As the water temperature increases, the pressure in the radiator rises but boiling cannot occur until the pressure of the spring is overcome. The valve is set to open at about 4 lb/in.[2] above atmospheric pressure and, at the increased pressure, the boiling point of water is some 12°F higher. The danger of boiling during a long climb on a hot day is therefore reduced considerably. If the car is being driven in a mountainous district at an altitude of 8,500 ft say, the atmospheric pressure will be about 4 lb/in.[2] lower than at sea-level and the water would normally boil at a temperature of only 196°F. Use of a 4 lb/in.[2] pressure cap restores the boiling point to the sea-level value of 212°F. The pressure cap includes a small relief valve to allow air to enter the radiator and prevent the creation of a partial vacuum when the engine cools.

### The Thermostat

An engine does not give its best performance until it has warmed up, partly because the petrol does not vaporize easily in a cold inlet manifold and partly because frictional losses are higher when the oil is cold and thick. Moreover, the rate of wear is very rapid during warming up compared with wear during steady running. Some of the wear can be attributed to the removal of the top surface of the metal which has

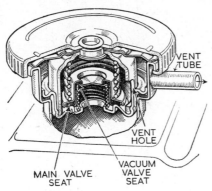

MAIN VALVE SEAT

VACUUM VALVE SEAT

VENT HOLE

VENT TUBE

*Fig. 9.8. Many radiators are fitted with pressure caps to reduce the risk of boiling. Steam can only escape when the pressure is sufficient to force the main valve off its seat*

corroded whilst the engine was standing idle. Further wear may result from the use of a very rich mixture during starting since some of the petrol may condense on the cold cylinder walls and dilute the lubricating oil.

It is therefore desirable to make the warming-up period as short as possible and this leads to the rather obvious idea of shutting off the flow of cooling water to the radiator. Most modern engines are fitted with an automatic valve known as a thermostat which is fitted somewhere in the water passage to the top of the radiator. During the warming-up period, the thermostat remains closed and the cooling water by-passes the radiator and re-circulates round the engine (Fig. 9.6(a) ). The thermostat is set to open at a temperature in the region of 140°–190°F. When this temperature is reached, the valve opens and the water flows through the radiator in the normal manner (Fig. 9.6(b) ). The movement of the thermostat valve is obtained by means of a concertina-like metal bellows filled with some liquid such as acetone which has a low boiling point. It is the vapour pressure of the liquid that causes the bellows to expand.

### The Water Thermometer

If an engine becomes overheated and the water boils, the driver soon becomes aware of steam issuing from the bonnet. He stops and allows the engine to cool down and no great harm is done. From this point

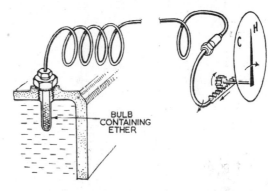

*Fig. 9.9. A vapour-pressure type water thermometer. The pressure of the ether increases as its temperature rises. The pressure is transmitted to a curved tube in the dial thermometer and the tube tends to uncurl, so turning the needle*

of view, a water thermometer is less important than an oil-pressure gauge. Nevertheless, a water thermometer is extremely useful. If the reading is high the driver knows that either he is driving too hard or there is something wrong with the engine— retarded ignition, perhaps, or a faulty exhaust valve, or the fan belt may be broken or slipping. A low reading shows that the engine may be over-cooled and that some form of radiator cover or perhaps a new thermostat is required.

Many water thermometers operate on the vapour-pressure principle. A metal bulb containing a liquid such as ether is placed in the hot water circuit and connected by a small-bore tube to a dial gauge on the instrument panel. The dial gauge is in fact a pressure gauge operating in the same way as the oil-pressure gauge described earlier. As the temperature of the ether rises, its vapour pressure increases and the coiled tube in the dial gauge tends to unwind, so turning the indicator needle (Fig. 9.9). The thermometer bulb is often mounted in the top of the radiator but this is unsatisfactory when a thermostat is used since the radiator temperature and engine temperature are no longer the same. A better place is in the cylinder head.

### Use of Anti-freeze

Freezing of the cooling water in cold weather can give rise to serious trouble. If the freezing is extensive, the flow of cooling water will be interrupted with the anomalous result that boiling occurs in the engine whilst ice blocks the radiator; there is also a danger of damage to the water pump. More serious, however, is the risk of damage to the cylinder block and cylinder head. Water has the unusual property of expanding as it freezes and the pressure set up in the water passages can be sufficient to crack the block or head. It is the freezing that does the damage, not the thawing as is often supposed, though the water does not gush from a burst pipe until the thaw sets in. Freezing can, of course, be avoided by draining the engine and radiator or by keeping a small lamp alight under the bonnet or beneath the engine, but these measures are unsuitable when the car is parked in the open. Moreover, freezing in the radiator can still occur on a very cold morning since, until the thermostat opens, the water in the radiator is stagnant while freezing air is drawn through the radiator by the fan. If a car is used frequently in winter, it is well worth mixing some anti-freeze solution with the cooling water.

Proprietary brands of anti-freeze consist of the liquid ethylene glycol with other substances added to prevent corrosion. The proportion of anti-freeze to be used depends on the degree of protection required. A 15 per cent solution gives protection against 24°F of frost and is sufficient during a normal English winter. The anti-freeze mixture does not have a sharply defined freezing point but becomes slushy before it solidifies. Besides having a lower freezing point than water, anti-freeze solution also has a higher boiling point and can therefore be left in the cooling system during the summer. It is not advisable to leave it in too long, however, owing to the fact that it is liable to deteriorate, and cause corrosion.

Chapter 10

# THE CLUTCH

THE clutch is a coupling between the engine and the transmission which is operated by a pedal with the driver's left foot. When the pedal is free, the coupling is engaged and the engine is linked through the transmission to the road wheels. When the pedal is depressed, the coupling or clutch is disengaged and the engine isolated. The engine is no longer in harness, so to speak, and if the accelerator is accidentally depressed, the engine revs away violently at the gallop. The clutch is the means of bringing its power gently under control. Although there is some trend towards replacement of the clutch *pedal* by automatic control (*see* Chapter 13), the clutch itself is likely to remain with us for many more years and the present chapter is devoted to a short account of its operation and construction.

### The Need for the Clutch

The usual positions of the engine, clutch, gear box and driving axle on a car with its engine in the normal front position are shown in Fig. 10.1. The necessity for some sort of clutch for isolating the engine from the road wheels is best appreciated by supposing the clutch to be missing. If the car is at rest and the gears are engaged, then the engine must also be at rest, since it is mechanically connected to the road wheels. Now a petrol engine cannot produce any torque (turning effort) whatsoever until it is turning at several hundred revolutions per minute (in this respect it is unlike the steam engine, certain electric motors and the gas turbine, all of which can be designed for high starting torque and do not need clutches). Evidently then, the car would be immobilized—it cannot start until the engine develops some torque, and the engine cannot develop any torque until the car has started. The only way it can possibly be started is by giving it a tow or running it down a hill. If the gears in the gear box are disengaged, the engine becomes mechanically free and can now be started and allowed to idle while the car remains at rest. This would appear to be a step forward, but this is not the case, for it is now almost impossible to re-engage the gears.  The engine is causing the gears to rotate, but nothing has been achieved until the output gear is coupled to the output shaft.  Bringing the dog-coupling into contact with the output gear would result in damage to the dog-teeth and a loud grating noise.  If we were successful in crashing the teeth into mesh, the engine would be jerked almost to

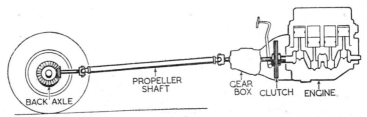

*Fig. 10.1.  General layout of the transmission of a car
with the normal front engine and rear-wheel drive*

rest and would then stall; the car would give a lurch forward, and would then stop.  It is the function of the clutch to overcome these difficulties.

### Principle of the Friction Clutch

Most cars use a clutch operating on the friction principle which can be explained by referring to Fig. 10.2.  The main component is a friction disc which is splined on to the input shaft of the gear box so that it turns with the shaft but is free to slide along it.  A strong spring presses the disc against the face of the engine flywheel and the friction between the two surfaces provides the only drive between the engine and the gear box.  When the clutch pedal is depressed, the pressure of the spring is overcome and the engine is mechanically isolated from the transmission.  Gears can now be engaged or changed and there is no danger of damaging the gear box since no power is being transmitted. The torque transmitted by friction depends on the pressure between the surfaces.  Gradual release of the clutch pedal ensures that the spring pressure is applied gradually so that the car accelerates smoothly from rest.  When the clutch pedal is fully released, the pressure between the friction disc and the flywheel is high enough to transmit the full torque of the engine without any slip occurring between the two surfaces.

### Construction of the Friction Clutch

While it would be possible for engine, clutch housing and gear box to be mounted separately on the chassis, the usual modern practice is for the three components to be connected together rigidly.  The clutch housing is bolted to the engine crankcase, and the gear box casing is either integral with the clutch housing or bolted to it.  This arrangement leads to a compact, light-weight design, and accurate alignment of the

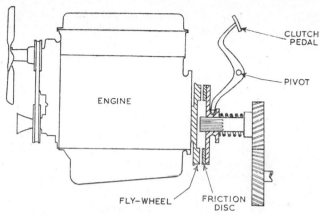

*Fig.* 10.2. *A simple friction clutch. When the clutch pedal is depressed, the friction drive between the flywheel and the friction disc is interrupted and the engine is isolated from the gear box*

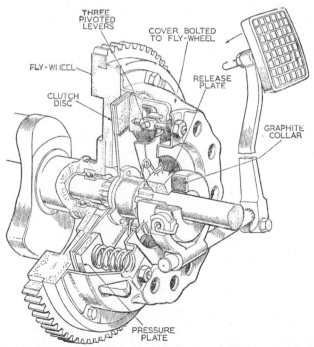

*Fig.* 10.3. *A modern friction clutch, slightly simplified. The clutch disc is gripped between the flywheel and the pressure plate, both of which rotate with the engine. When the clutch pedal is depressed, the release plate acts on three pivoted levers; the pressure plate is pulled back on to the springs, so freeing the clutch disc and isolating the engine from the gear box*

components is obtained so that there is no need for a flexible coupling between the clutch and gear box.

The construction of a typical modern friction clutch is somewhat more elaborate than that of the simplified clutch referred to above but the basic principle is very similar. The friction or clutch disc slides on an extension of the gear-box input shaft as before and torque is transmitted from the flywheel to the disc by means of friction (Fig. 10.3). Instead of a large single spring, however, several smaller springs are used and these are located in a cover which is bolted to the flywheel and rotates with it. The springs do not bear directly on the clutch disc but act through a pressure plate which is free to slide on three pins attached to the cover. Thus the clutch disc is held in a double grip between the flywheel on the one side and the pressure plate on the other. This arrangement has the advantage that torque is transmitted not only from the face of the flywheel but also through the pressure plate which is indirectly attached to the flywheel. Both sides of the friction disc are faced with a special material containing asbestos and designed to combine high frictional resistance with good heat resistance and low wear.

To disengage the clutch, it is necessary to withdraw the pressure plate from contact with the clutch disc by drawing it back against the springs. The actuating force comes, of course, from the driver's foot acting on the clutch pedal but the process can be seen better by starting at the other end. Three small levers are pivoted to the clutch cover, their outer ends gripping corresponding lips in the pressure plate and their inner ends making contact with a sliding release plate. When this release plate is pushed towards the flywheel, the levers turn on their pivots and the pressure plate is withdrawn against the springs. The levers, springs, pivots, cover and release plate form a single unit which rotates with the flywheel. The depression of the clutch pedal is translated into a horizontal movement of the release plate. To avoid friction and wear due to the relative motion, the pressure is applied through a graphite collar or a ball thrust bearing.

It is very desirable that there should be some flexibility in the drive between the engine and transmission, partly to prevent engine vibrations from harming the transmission and partly to protect the whole mechanism from shock when the driver inadvertently releases the clutch too quickly. This flexibility is usually achieved by incorporating cushion springs in the clutch disc itself between the outer friction disc and the splined hub (Fig. 10.4).

It is interesting to note that the clutch assembly is quite independent of its housing. The clutch shaft is supported in the gear box at one end and by a bearing in the centre of the engine flywheel at the other whilst the clutch cover, which houses the clutch assembly, is bolted to the flywheel. The main function of the housing is to support the gear box. So far as the clutch is concerned, it serves only as a location for the clutch pedal linkage and a protection against dirt.

A clutch of the type described above is referred to as a single-plate friction clutch. Some clutches are designed to use several friction

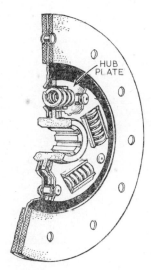

*Fig.* 10.4. *On the modern clutch disc, the drive from the friction surfaces to the hub is taken through cushion springs. These protect the transmission against engine vibrations and against shock due to sudden engagement of the clutch*

discs in order to increase the torque that can be transmitted without the size and weight of the unit becoming excessive.

The modern clutch will stand much rough handling and should have a life of some tens of thousands of miles, given a little care and attention. There is enough compression in the springs for them to take up wear of the friction linings without the pressure becoming too small. As wear takes place, the free play of the clutch pedal tends to be taken up and needs to be restored by adjusting the linkage. A movement of ½ in. or so is usually allowed before the clutch starts to disengage. If this free play is absent, there may be a residual force in the pedal linkage which can prevent the clutch from fully engaging and cause unnecessary wear of the graphite release collar or thrust bearing. Wear of this collar is also increased by keeping the foot on the clutch pedal and leaving the engine in gear during short halts.

### Hydraulic Control

On modern cars, the direct mechanical link between the clutch pedal and the clutch release lever is often replaced by a hydraulic control system similar to that now used universally for the brakes (Fig. 10.5).

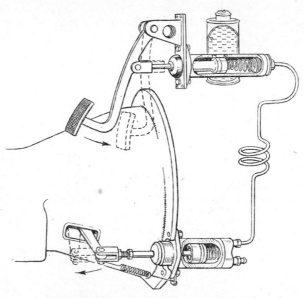

*Fig.* 10.5. *Hydraulic clutch control. The mechanical linkage between the clutch pedal and the clutch is replaced by a hydraulic system similar to that used for hydraulic brake operation*

When the clutch pedal is depressed, the piston in the master cylinder moves forward and the oil in the system is compressed to a high pressure. The pressure is transmitted through a small bore pipe which links the master cylinder to a slave cylinder mounted at the side of the clutch housing. The oil pressure causes the slave piston to move rearwards so operating the clutch release lever. Apart from the method of control, a hydraulically controlled clutch operates in the same way as one controlled by a mechanical linkage.

---

# Chapter 11

# MAKING USE OF THE ENGINE

THE engine of a car will only function correctly while the engine speed is within its normal range of operation. The wheel speed, of course, varies continuously with the speed of the car, and for this reason the engine of a motor car is never coupled directly to the wheel axle.

In order to make the best use of the engine, it must be coupled to the road wheels through gearing and a range of gears must be provided to ensure the best performance throughout the speed range of the vehicle. Hence a car must have a reduction gear (usually fitted in the back axle) and a gear box. The reasons for this are discussed in the first part of this chapter and then, after some notes on gear wheels, the gear box itself is dealt with. The chapter concludes with a discussion of the use of overdrives, which are becoming increasingly popular.

### Need to Reduce Engine Speed

Most of the petrol engines used in motor cars are designed to run at maximum speeds of between 4,000 and 5,000 r.p.m. The engine delivers its maximum torque or turning effort at some 2,500 r.p.m. and spends much of its useful life running in the range of 2,000–3,000 r.p.m. The speed of rotation of the road wheels, however, when the car is travelling at 75 m.p.h. is only 1,100 r.p.m. or so, whilst for much of the time the wheel speed is considerably lower. If the engine crankshaft were directly coupled to the wheel axle, the engine would be obliged to run at the same speed, and would never be able to deliver its full power (*see* left side of Fig. 11.1). The power developed by the engine at, say, 75 m.p.h., that is, at about 1,100 r.p.m., would be less than the power required for propelling the car and, consequently, the car would slow down. The engine would therefore run at an even lower speed and its power would be further reduced. The car would slow down further and the sequence of events would repeat itself until the car stopped.

The difficulty is overcome by introducing a reduction gear between the engine crankshaft and the wheel axle. This gear, the crown wheel

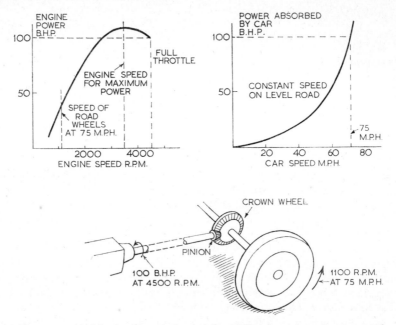

Fig. 11.1.   *Need for the crown wheel and pinion.   When the car is moving at 75 m.p.h. the wheels are turning at about 1,100 r.p.m.   The power required to propel the car is 100 b.h.p. (say), and the engine must therefore run at about 4,500 r.p.m.   The crown wheel and pinion provide the required reduction of speed from 4,500 to 1,100 r.p.m.*

and pinion, is usually incorporated in the back axle.   When the engine is in top gear, the gear box is, in effect, short-circuited, and the only speed reduction between the engine and road wheels is that due to the crown wheel and pinion.   Let us suppose that the engine develops a power of 100 b.h.p. at its maximum speed of 4,500 r.p.m.   The power-speed curve for the vehicle is shown on the right-hand side of Fig. 11.1, from which it is seen that 100 b.h.p. is sufficient to propel the car at 75 m.p.h. or 6,600 ft/min.   If the road wheels are 2 ft in diameter with a circumference of about 6 ft, the speed of the road wheels at 75 m.p.h. is $\frac{6,600}{6}$ or 1,100 r.p.m.   The required ratio for the back axle reduction gear is therefore $\frac{4,500}{1,100}$ or 4·09.   The ratio for most cars is between 3·5 and 5·0.   The construction of the crown wheel and pinion unit will be dealt with in the next chapter.

### The Need for the Gear Box

Without a change-speed gear box, the speed of the engine can have only one value for any given road speed.   It is as though the engine were always in top gear.  Now a car behaves perfectly well in top gear provided the road speed is fairly high and the gradient of the road is not too steep.  If, however, the driver tries to accelerate from a low speed, 15 m.p.h. say, in top gear, he finds the acceleration is very poor. The reason for this, of course, is that the engine speed is low and therefore the power is also low.  In the example in the last section, the engine speed at 75 m.p.h. was 4,500 r.p.m.  Clearly the engine speed at 15 m.p.h. or one fifth of maximum speed would be $\frac{4,500}{5}$ or 900 r.p.m. It can be seen from Fig. 11.1 that the engine power at this speed is rather small.  A gear box is therefore required to enable the engine speed to be stepped up when the speed of the car is low, thus ensuring good acceleration.

To obtain the maximum possible acceleration over the whole range of road speed, it would be necessary to operate the engine at maximum power all the time, i.e. at an engine speed of about 4,000 r.p.m.  To achieve this condition, we would have to vary the gear-box ratio continuously according to the road speed.  Suppose that the road speed corresponding to 4,000 r.p.m. with direct drive to the back axle is 70 m.p.h.  Then to keep the engine speed at 4,000 r.p.m. when the car is moving at 35 m.p.h., a gear-box ratio of 2 : 1 is required.  The following table gives the ratios required throughout the speed range:

**Table 5.  Gear-box Ratios**

| Road speed, m.p.h. | 10 | 20 | 30 | 40 | 50 | 60 | 70 |
|---|---|---|---|---|---|---|---|
| Gear-box ratio to give engine speed of 4,000 r.p.m. | 7·0 | 3·5 | 2·3 | 1·75 | 1·4 | 1·17 | 1·0 |

No satisfactory gear box has yet been devised to give a continuous variation of speed ratio over such a wide range.  The modern automobile gear box is a compromise in which 2 or 3 gear ratios are provided in addition to the top gear or 1 : 1 ratio and each ratio covers a part of the speed range.

**Some Notes on Gear Wheels**

The function of a pair of gear wheels is to transmit power between two shafts moving at different speeds; a pair of pulleys and a belt does the same thing (*see* Fig. 11.2).  The advantage of gearing is that it is more compact and more efficient.  The power that can be transmitted by a pulley belt is small compared with that transmitted by a pair of gears occupying the same space, and the rate of wear of the belt is comparatively high.  The pulley system relies on friction for the

5

transmission of power whereas, with gear wheels, it is the positive pressure between the teeth that produces the drive.

The speed ratio of a pair of gears is determined by the ratio of the number of teeth on the two wheels as can be seen from Fig. 11.2. Since the tooth size is the same for both wheels, the wheel with the greater number of teeth is the larger in diameter. In fact, the ratio of the diameters is the same as the ratio of the number of teeth.

The shape of the teeth is designed to ensure that one tooth rolls over the other as the wheels rotate. There is very little sliding or friction and the power loss is therefore very low; for our present purposes, we can say that the input power equals the output power. The torque, however, is changed according to the diameters of the wheels. This

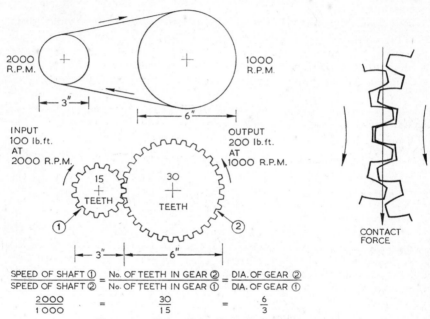

$$\frac{\text{SPEED OF SHAFT } \textcircled{1}}{\text{SPEED OF SHAFT } \textcircled{2}} = \frac{\text{No. OF TEETH IN GEAR } \textcircled{2}}{\text{No. OF TEETH IN GEAR } \textcircled{1}} = \frac{\text{DIA. OF GEAR } \textcircled{2}}{\text{DIA. OF GEAR } \textcircled{1}}$$

$$\frac{2000}{1000} = \frac{30}{15} = \frac{6}{3}$$

Fig. 11.2. *Gear wheels, like pulleys, can be used to reduce speed and increase torque. But gear wheels can transmit far more power since they depend on positive tooth pressure instead of on a belt which is liable to slip*

can be explained by considering the transfer of power between the teeth in contact (Fig. 11.2). The torque in either wheel due to the force between the teeth can be compared with the torque produced by a man turning a capstan. As was explained in Chapter 2, the torque or turning effort is obtained by multiplying the force by the radius. The force is the same for both wheels but since the second wheel is twice as large as the first, the torque is doubled whilst the speed is halved.

The way in which this principle is applied to assist a car in climbing a steep hill can be illustrated by considering a very simple 2-speed gear box (Fig. 11.3). When the gear lever is in position 1, gears A and B are engaged. If the car encounters a steep hill, a greater turning

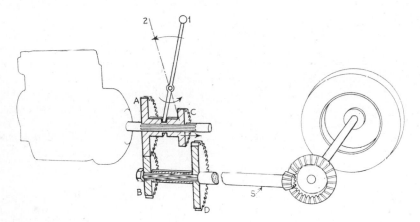

Fig. 11.3. (Above) A simple 2-speed gear box. With A and B in mesh, S rotates faster than the engine but the torque is only sufficient on a level road. With C and D in mesh, S rotates more slowly but the torque is increased and the car can tackle a gradient

Fig. 11.4. (Right) Spur teeth have been largely superseded by helical teeth in modern gear boxes. Helical teeth are quieter in operation and will withstand higher loading

SPUR        HELICAL

effort is required at the road wheels and in the output shaft S. The gears C and D are therefore brought into mesh by shifting the lever to the second position. Gear D is much larger than gear C and the output torque is therefore greatly increased. The car now has considerably more " pull " though the engine has to turn faster than before to maintain a given road speed.

Gears having " straight " teeth, that is teeth cut parallel to the shaft, are known as straight-cut or spur gears (Fig. 11.4). This type of gearing has been very largely replaced by helical gears whose teeth are cut at an angle to form part of a curve known as a helix. Helical teeth will

123

withstand higher loading and are quieter in operation due to the smoother engagement of the teeth.

### The " Crash " Gear Box

Before describing the modern gear box a few remarks about its predecessors are desirable.  As we have seen, the gear box is only required when the car is travelling at low speed or up a hill or when the car is accelerating; at high speed, a direct coupling between the engine and the transmission shaft is desirable.  This cannot be achieved in the simple type of gear box shown in Fig. 11.3 and it was superseded by the " crash " type shown in Fig. 11.5.  As with the modern gear box, the gear on the engine input shaft meshes with a gear on a layshaft and, except in top gear, this shaft re-transmits the power through a second pair of gears.  It is the second pair that can be varied to give the different ratios by sliding the gears on the output shaft into and out of mesh.  The special advantage of this arrangement is that top gear is provided by a direct " dog " type coupling between the input and output shafts.  In top gear, no power is transmitted through the layshaft gearing and a very quiet drive is obtained.

The disadvantage of the " crash " gear box is implied in its name.  The gears have to be slid into mesh while turning and considerable skill is needed to ensure that the two wheels are turning at approximately the same tooth speed; if they are not, one wheel will grate on the other and the wear and tear on both gear wheels and nerves will be excessive.  The difficulty is overcome in the modern gear box by use of constant mesh gearing combined with synchromesh gear changing.

### Constant Mesh Gearing

The first step towards silent gear changing was the introduction of constant mesh gearing.  The principle of this is illustrated in Fig. 11.6.  On a crash type gear box, only gears A and B would be in constant mesh and C and D would be slid into mesh when required (it would be difficult to do this unless straight tooth gears were used).  With the arrangement shown, C and D are constantly in mesh.  The gear D forms an integral part of the layshaft but the gear C rotates freely on the output shaft until the dog coupling is moved to the right.  The dog coupling is splined to the output shaft; that is, it is keyed to the shaft and must rotate with it, but it can slide along the shaft.  When the teeth of the dog coupling engage with the corresponding teeth on the gear C, the drive is taken through all four gears.  When the dog coupling is shifted to the left it engages with the teeth on the input gear and the input and output shafts are directly coupled; gear C then rotates freely.  The advantage of this system is that the gears cannot be damaged during gear changing. It is true that the wear is now transferred to the dog teeth but this does not affect the smoothness of operation in the way that wear of the gear teeth themselves would. Also, when two gear wheels are brought into mesh, the teeth near the meshing point take all the shock, whereas with the dog coupling, all the dog teeth are engaged simultaneously and the load is well shared. The net result is that the

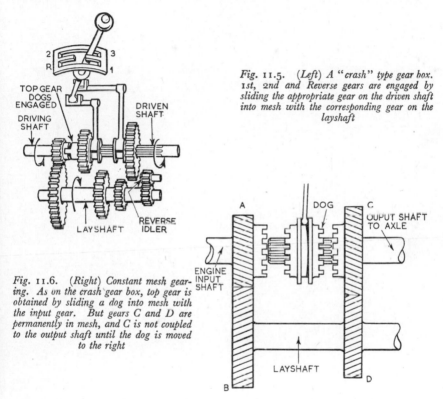

Fig. 11.5. (Left) A "crash" type gear box. 1st, 2nd and Reverse gears are engaged by sliding the appropriate gear on the driven shaft into mesh with the corresponding gear on the layshaft

Fig. 11.6. (Right) Constant mesh gearing. As on the crash gear box, top gear is obtained by sliding a dog into mesh with the input gear. But gears C and D are permanently in mesh, and C is not coupled to the output shaft until the dog is moved to the right

gears are easier to engage and the gear box is quieter since helical gears can be used.

### The Synchromesh Gear Box

The last stage in the development of the modern gear box was the introduction of the synchromesh principle. The idea was to use constant mesh gearing of the type just described but to employ " synchromesh " for ensuring smooth engagement of the dog teeth. Various types of synchromesh are in use but the principle is the same in each case. The final engagement of the dog coupling with the corresponding dog teeth

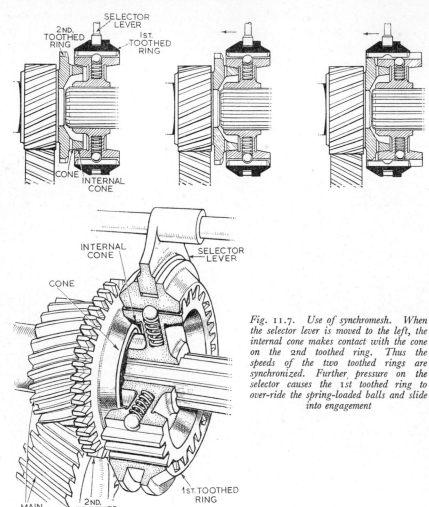

*Fig. 11.7. Use of synchromesh. When the selector lever is moved to the left, the internal cone makes contact with the cone on the 2nd toothed ring. Thus the speeds of the two toothed rings are synchronized. Further pressure on the selector causes the 1st toothed ring to over-ride the spring-loaded balls and slide into engagement*

of the gear wheel is preceded by a frictional contact which synchronizes the speeds of the coupling and the gear wheel and enables the dog teeth to slide together quietly.

One popular arrangement is shown in Fig. 11.7. The sliding dog coupling labelled " 1st toothed ring " has its teeth cut internally. Instead of sliding directly on the output shaft, its teeth engage with the internal cone wheel. When the dog coupling is moved to the left by operation of the selector fork it carries the internal cone wheel with it, the motion being transmitted through the spring-loaded balls mounted in the internal cone. The latter has conical faces cut internally on both sides of it; as the cone wheel moves to the left, the left-hand face mates with a conical surface cut on the side of the second toothed ring attached to the gear wheel. The frictional contact between the two cones tends to synchronize the speeds of the gear wheel and dog coupling. When further pressure is applied to the gear change lever, the dog coupling rides over the balls in the internal cone wheel and engages silently with the gear wheel dog teeth, because the two are now rotating at the same speed.

The use of constant mesh gearing on a modern 3-speed gear box is illustrated in Fig. 11.8. Synchromesh is used on all three gears but not

*Fig. 11.8. A modern 3-speed gear box. Constant mesh gears and synchromesh engagement are used for all three forward speeds. Reverse is engaged by sliding the straight-toothed gear into mesh with the reverse idler*

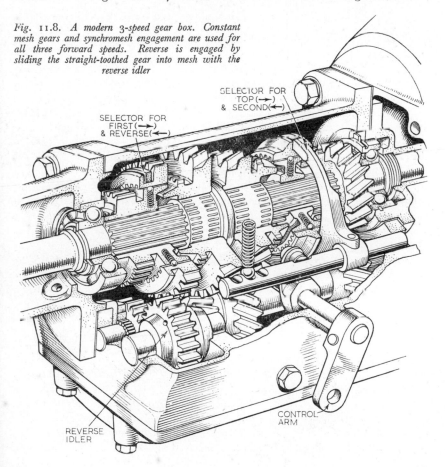

SELECTOR FOR
TOP (→)
& SECOND(←)

SELECTOR FOR
FIRST (→)
& REVERSE(←)

CONTROL
ARM

REVERSE
IDLER

on reverse. Four-speed boxes usually employ synchromesh for the top three forward ratios but use sliding mesh gears for bottom gear and reverse. For a given engine and vehicle, a 4-speed box will permit a livelier performance, since the greater the number of gear ratios, the nearer the engine can be run to its maximum power over the entire speed range of the car.

With a 4-speed box, maximum engine power can be developed at four different forward speeds of the car, whereas a 3-speed box only provides maximum power at three forward speeds. The car speeds at which maximum power is available are determined by the ratios of the gears. If, for example, maximum power is developed at an engine speed of 4,000 r.p.m. and the corresponding road speed in top gear is 70 m.p.h., then a gear ratio of 2 : 1 would provide maximum power at a speed of $\dfrac{70}{2}$ or 35 m.p.h. The acceleration at 35 m.p.h. would then be as great as was possible with that particular engine.

Fig. 11.9 shows the positions of the gears and dogs in a 3-speed box for the three forward gears and for reverse. During a change from a high gear to a lower one, the clutch disc is speeded up by the transmission whilst disengaged. The change is therefore made more smoothly if the engine is accelerated slightly before the clutch is re-engaged. The question does not arise, however, when changing gear in the opposite direction. To avoid damage to the dog teeth, gears must only be changed when the gear box is transmitting no power; this condition is normally satisfied, of course, by disengaging the clutch. It is, however, possible to achieve the same requirement by holding the accelerator at the point where the engine is neither delivering power nor acting as a brake on the transmission. Thus with skilful use of the throttle, clutchless gear changes are possible.

When reducing speed, the engine can be used as a brake by changing to a lower gear and letting the car drive the engine. If one takes the right foot off the brake in order to rev the engine in the manner mentioned above, a second or two of braking time is lost. With suitable positioning of the brake and throttle, however, the two actions can be performed simultaneously by the right foot, using the " heel-and-toe " technique.

### Use of an Overdrive

An overdrive is a compact gear unit fitted in the transmission between the gear box and the rear axle. Its effect is to reduce the engine speed for any particular speed of the car. Suppose, for example, that the engine speed in top gear at 50 m.p.h. is 3,000 r.p.m.; when an overdrive is used the engine speed will be about 25 per cent lower at the same road speed, that is about 2,250 r.p.m. On a long fast journey, overdrive enables a high cruising speed to be combined with a quiet slow-running engine.   At low revs, the frictional losses in the engine are reduced and some gain in fuel consumption can therefore be expected.   There may also be some reduction in the rate of engine wear but it is doubtful whether this particular gain is very great.   The effect of an overdrive could of course be achieved by using a lower axle ratio.   Changing the axle ratio from 4 to 3 would produce the same effect as the overdrive

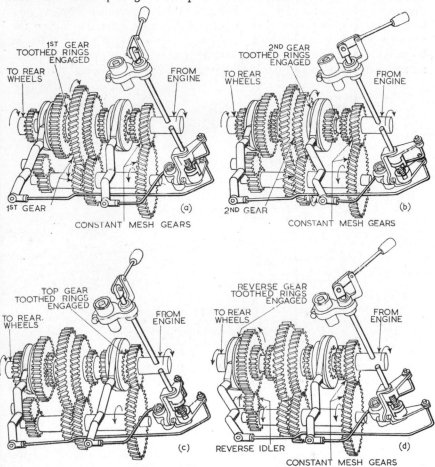

Fig. 11.9.   *Operating positions of a 3-speed gear box with steering column control:*
(a) *first gear engaged*
(b) *second gear engaged*
(c) *top gear engaged*
(d) *reverse gear engaged*

in the example just mentioned. The reduced axle ratio, however, would affect the performance of the car over the whole range of operation since it cannot be conveniently switched in and out in the same way as an overdrive. The limitation on engine speed would apply even during acceleration and there would be an inevitable loss in performance.

The effect of an overdrive can be explained in another way by referring back to Fig. 11.1. From the graph on the right we see that the car requires about 50 h.p. in order to cruise at 60 m.p.h. If we now look at the engine power curve on the left, we see that the engine can develop this power at quite a low speed—about 1,750 r.p.m. But at 60 m.p.h. in top gear the engine speed is about 3,600 r.p.m. (assuming an axle ratio of 4·09 and a wheel diameter of 2 ft, as before); the power

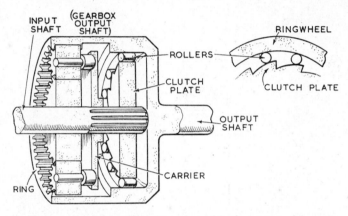

*Fig. 11.10. Overdrive. The unit can be used in three ways:—(1) centre (sun) wheel held stationary: speed is stepped-up; (2) centre wheel locked to carrier or to ring: solid drive; (3) centre wheel free to rotate on input shaft: solid drive when engine develops power, free-wheel on over-run*

available considerably exceeds the power required and the engine must therefore run with a fairly small throttle opening. When an overdrive is used, the power required for a particular road speed is unchanged, but the engine produces it at a lower speed and wider throttle opening. This leads to improved efficiency, since the wider throttle opening leads to a higher compression pressure.

Both the Borg-Warner and the Laycock de Normanville overdrives are of epicyclic design. An epicyclic gear train differs from normal gearing in that the centres of some of the gears are not fixed. On the unit shown in Fig. 11.10, two small " planet " wheels mesh with a central " sun " wheel and also with an internally cut ring wheel. The planets are mounted on a carrier which is splined to the input shaft and rotates with it. The ring wheel is mounted on the output shaft leading to the back axle. The sun wheel is carried on the input shaft but is free to rotate independently when required. In addition to the gear wheels, the unit incorporates a one-way roller clutch; the clutch plate is splined to the gear-box shaft and can transmit power to the ring wheel through the wedging action of the rollers but only in one direction. The whole unit is enclosed in a housing which is bolted to the gear box.

An epicyclic overdrive unit of this sort can be made to operate in various ways by controlling the movement of the sun wheel. The essential requirement is that both normal drive and overdrive are obtainable. The method of control may be hydraulic or electric and can be made semi-automatic by linking the control to the movement of the accelerator and by other means. It is usual for the driver to be able to select or cut out the overdrive action by operating a panel control.

If the sun wheel is locked to the carrier, the planet wheels are prevented from rotating; the whole gear train is locked solid and normal drive is obtained. The drive is transmitted from the input to the output shaft via the interlocked sun, planet and ring gears. On the Borg-Warner unit direct drive is obtained in this way. A similar result is achieved on the Laycock de Normanville overdrive by locking the sun wheel to the ring gear via a cone clutch (not shown in Fig. 11.10).

When the sun wheel is completely free to rotate on the input shaft, no power can be transmitted through the gear train. If the engine is developing power and tending to propel the car, direct drive is experienced because of the wedging action of the clutch rollers. When the driver lifts his foot from the accelerator, the output shaft and ring wheel tend to override the input shaft and clutch plate; the rollers are no longer wedged and the car freewheels in the same way as a bicycle. This method of operation is employed in the Borg-Warner overdrive for road speeds below 27 m.p.h. As the engine and vehicle are isolated during free-wheeling, gear changing can be carried out simply by releasing the accelerator; the clutch need not be used.

Overdrive action is obtained by holding the sun wheel stationary; this can be done by locking the wheel to the casing. In this position, the planet wheels revolve round the sun wheel and transmit the drive to the ring wheel and output shaft. The step-up in speed from the input to the output shaft is in the ratio 3 : 4 approximately. Epicyclic gearing is discussed further in Chapter 14 in connection with automatic gear boxes.

# Chapter 12

---

# THE DRIVE TO THE ROAD WHEELS

WHEN an engine is used for generating electricity or propelling a boat there is no difficulty in transmitting the power; the output shaft is coupled directly to the dynamo or the propeller as the case may be. When the engine is used for driving a car, however, certain mechanical problems have to be overcome. In the first place, the car is mounted on springs, so the drive from the engine to the wheels must allow for considerable relative movement. Secondly, the engine crankshaft usually runs from front to rear and the wheel axles are therefore at right angles to it; the drive must therefore be turned through a right angle. Moreover, when the car is turning a corner, the outside wheels tend to move faster than the inside ones and the power must therefore be transmitted at two slightly different speeds.

The present chapter discusses how these difficulties are overcome, with emphasis on the traditional engine-in-front, rear-wheel drive design. At the end of the chapter rear engines and front-wheel drives are also referred to.

### From Gear Box to Back Axle

On practically all British and American cars the engine is mounted at the front of the vehicle and the power is transmitted through a long propelling shaft to the rear wheels. The car is pushed along by the rear wheels, steered by the front wheels and supported by all four. The engine, clutch and gear box form a self-contained unit which is directly mounted on the chassis or body. In order to minimize the transmission of engine noise and vibration to the vehicle as a whole, the mountings are designed for a certain amount of flexibility. The main effect of the flexibility, however, is to allow the engine to move about the crankshaft and absorb fluctuations in torque; the amount of fore-and-aft and up-and-down movement permitted is fairly small.

The back axle, on the other hand, is attached to the body or chassis through a pair of leaf springs (*see* Fig. 12.1) and when the car goes over a bump the up-and-down movement of the back axle in relation to the body is considerable. If the gear-box output shaft and the back-axle input shaft were coupled together stiffly as in Fig. 12.2, there would be a bending action on the propelling shaft and failure would soon result. To overcome the difficulty the rigid couplings are replaced by universal joints based on the Hooke coupling. A Hooke coupling permits two shafts whose centre lines intersect at the coupling to have relative angular movement (Fig. 12.3). Use of two Hooke couplings permits relative parallel displacement as well; there will be no strain in the shafting even though the centre lines do not intersect at the coupling.

The modern universal joint is very much more compact than the Hooke coupling but it operates in the same way. The cross-piece or "spider", which forms the link between the two shafts, runs in needle-

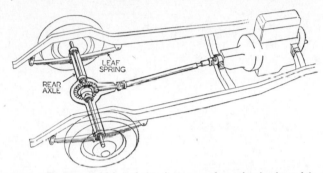

*Fig. 12.1. On most British and American cars, the engine is situated in front and the drive is transmitted to the rear wheels through a long propeller shaft. The rear of the car rests on a pair of leaf springs which are bolted to the rear axle casing*

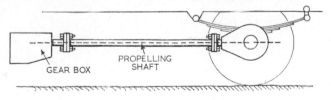

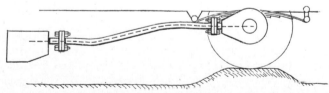

*Fig. 12.2. If the propelling shaft were bolted rigidly to the gear box and rear axle as shown in this diagram, it would be subject to severe bending whenever the car passed over a bump*

roller bearings. The spider is hollow and is provided with a grease nipple for occasional lubrication (*see* Fig. 12.4). Alternatively the four arms of the spider may be mounted in rubber bushes, in which the universal joints require no lubrication (Fig. 12.5).

There is a further relative movement between the gear box and back axle that has to be provided for in the transmission. The back axle casing is rigidly clamped to the rear springs and normally the front

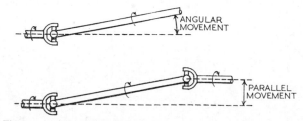

*Fig.* 12.3. (*Above*) *The difficulty illustrated in Fig.* 12.2 *can be overcome by using a pair of Hooke couplings. The ends of the propelling shaft can then have both angular and parallel movement relative to one another*

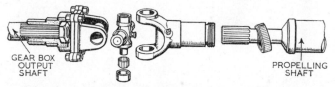

*Fig.* 12.4. *Details of a universal joint designed to act as a Hooke coupling. A cross-piece or " spider " links the two halves of the coupling. Friction is reduced by the use of needle-roller bearings*

end of the spring is pivoted to the frame while the rear end is attached through a link; this arrangement allows the increased length of the spring to be accommodated when the spring flexes. A secondary effect, however, is that, whilst the propeller shaft pivots about the front universal joint, the rear axle pivots about the front spring pin; as a result, the distance between the gear box and back axle alters slightly (*see* Fig. 12.6). To allow for the change in length, a sliding joint is included in the transmission.

With the open propeller shaft arrangement just described, the rear springs serve a double function. Besides supporting the weight of the car flexibly, the springs must also transmit to the car the push exerted by the wheels on the road surface. If the springs are stiff enough for the second job they may be too stiff for the first. The difficulty is sometimes overcome by mounting both ends of the springs freely on links and taking the force through a stiff tube which encloses the propeller shaft (Fig. 12.7). This torque tube also takes the reaction of the torque

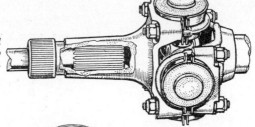

Fig. 12.5. *(Right) This universal joint uses clamped rubber bushes to supply the required relative movement. It needs no lubrication*

RUBBER BUSH

Fig. 12.6. *(Below) When the rear axle moves vertically in relation to the body, the axle turns in a small radius A about the front spring attachment Q. The end of the propeller shaft, on the other hand, turns in a large radius B about the front coupling P. A sliding joint has therefore to be provided to accommodate the difference in movement*

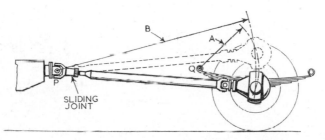

B

A

Q

P

SLIDING JOINT

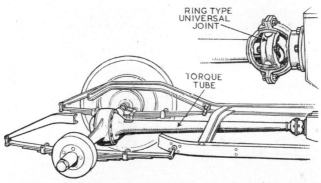

RING TYPE UNIVERSAL JOINT

TORQUE TUBE

Fig. 12.7. *On most popular cars the "push" from the rear wheels to the body is taken through the springs. A rigid torque tube enclosing the propeller shaft is sometimes used to relieve the springs of this secondary duty. The springs are shackled at front and rear, instead of at one end only. The inset shows a universal joint using a ring instead of a cross-piece*

135

from the rear wheels, a further duty that must usually be performed by the springs. The tube is bolted rigidly to the back axle and is attached to the gear-box casing via a ball and socket joint. With this arrangement, the only relative movement between the back axle and the gear box is a simple angular one; no sliding movement takes place and a single universal joint located at the gear-box end is all that is required.

### The Crown Wheel and Pinion

One of the functions of the back-axle driving gear, namely the reduction of shaft speed, has been dealt with in Chapter 11. The second function is the obvious one of producing a right-angled drive, since the propelling

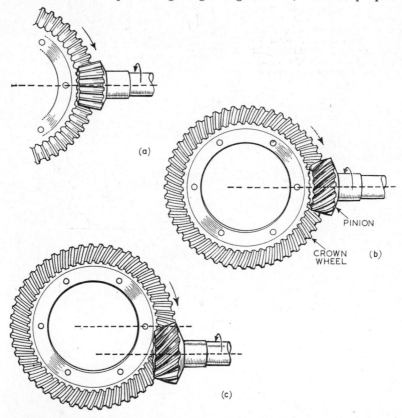

*Fig.* 12.8. *The rear-axle crown-wheel and pinion perform the dual function of speed reduction and right-angled drive. Straight bevel teeth (a) are simplest. Spiral bevel teeth (b) are quieter and stronger. Hypoid teeth (c) permit a lower propeller shaft*

shaft and the rear axle are at right angles. The simplest form of gearing to fulfil these two functions is a pair of straight bevel gears (Fig. 12.8). But just as helical gears are superior to straight spur gears for use in gear boxes, so spiral bevel gears have proved superior to straight bevels, both in strength and smoothness of running. The larger gear is known as the crown wheel and the smaller one as the pinion. As with gears used in gear boxes, the speed ratio of bevel gearing is equal to the ratio of the numbers of teeth. If, for instance, the crown wheel has 40 teeth and the pinion 10, the axle ratio is 4 : 1.

Spiral bevel gears are now giving way to a type of gear known as a hypoid. The main difference between the two is that, with hypoid gearing, the axis of the pinion shaft is located below the axle centre line (Fig. 12.8). This feature reduces the height of the propeller shaft and thus permits a lower floor level in the rear compartment. The axle gears are lubricated by running them in a bath of heavy oil stored in the casing below the crown wheel. With hypoid gearing, there is a sliding as well as a rolling motion between the teeth and this makes the lubrication requirements more stringent. Special " extreme pressure " hypoid oils have been developed for this application.

### The Rear Axle

Except when independent rear suspension is used, the rear axle, rear wheels and crown wheel and pinion form an integral unit attached to the car through a pair of leaf springs. The unit derives its strength from the axle housing which consists of a central box containing the crown wheel and pinion and two tubular extensions for supporting the wheels and shafts (Fig. 12.9). The " live " part of the axle, that is the shaft linking the crown wheel to the wheels, transmits torque and does not carry any appreciable weight. Because of the need for differential wheel speed (discussed below), the shaft is in two halves. Serving a limited purpose as it does, each half-shaft is quite small in diameter. The whole axle assembly is often referred to as a " live axle ".

The bearing arrangement shown in Fig. 12.9 is for a " semi-floating " axle. The " semi " indicates that the shaft has to carry weight as well as torque; this is because the wheel is bolted directly to the half-shaft flange. On a " fully floating " axle, the wheel is bolted to a hub which runs on bearings attached only to the axle housing. The half-shafts are splined into the wheel hubs so that the connection is a sliding one and torque alone can be transmitted. This arrangement eases the task both of the half-shafts and of the bearings. The second arrangement shown in Fig. 12.9 is for a " three-quarter floating axle ". In this case the wheel is bolted to a hub *and* to the half-shaft flange. Most of the weight is carried through the hub though a small amount can be

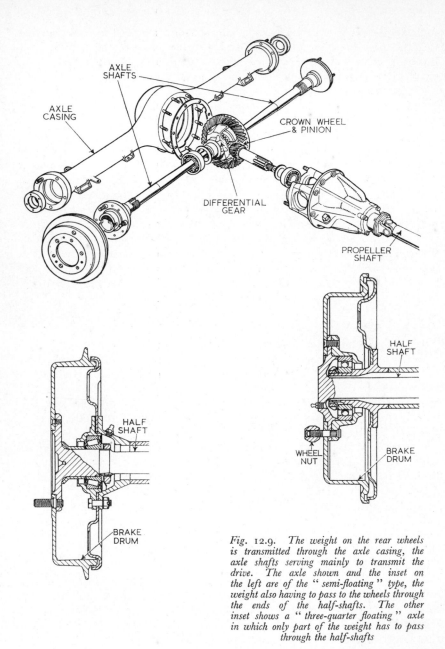

AXLE
SHAFTS

AXLE
CASING

CROWN WHEEL
& PINION

DIFFERENTIAL
GEAR

PROPELLER
SHAFT

HALF
SHAFT

HALF
SHAFT

WHEEL
NUT

BRAKE
DRUM

BRAKE
DRUM

*Fig.* 12.9.    *The weight on the rear wheels
is transmitted through the axle casing, the
axle shafts serving mainly to transmit the
drive.    The axle shown and the inset on
the left are of the " semi-floating " type, the
weight also having to pass to the wheels through
the ends of the half-shafts.    The other
inset shows a " three-quarter floating " axle
in which only part of the weight has to pass
through the half-shafts*

taken through the half-shafts to the inner bearings adjacent to the crown wheel.

### The Differential

The differential consists of a cluster of two or four small bevel gears located inside the crown wheel in the back axle. The need for the differential arises when the car is cornering. The car in Fig. 12.10 is turning a corner of 30 ft radius at 30 m.p.h.; the " track " of the car,

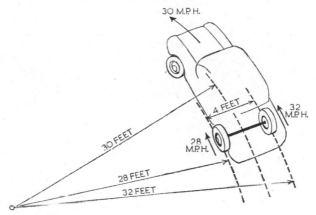

*Fig. 12.10. When a car turns a corner, the inner and outer wheels travel and rotate at different speeds*

that is the distance between the rear (or the front) wheels is 4 ft. The rear wheel on the inside of the curve is therefore moving round a curve of 28 ft radius and the outside wheel round a curve of 32 ft radius. And since a 30 ft radius corresponds to 30 m.p.h., the inner and outer wheel speeds must be 28 m.p.h. and 32 m.p.h. If, however, the two half-shafts of the back axle were bolted rigidly to the crown wheel as shown on the left in Fig. 12.11, the two rear wheels would be obliged to turn at the same speed. Slipping would occur between the tyres and the road and this would result in waste of power and excessive tyre wear.

The differential gear (Fig. 12.11) is an ingenious device for overcoming this difficulty. Each of the half-shafts carries a bevel gear which meshes with a pair of bevel pinions. The pinions are carried in bearings which are attached to the crown wheel and rotate with it. The pinion on the propeller shaft turns the crown wheel in the normal way. When the car is moving in a straight line, there is normally no tendency for one wheel to rotate faster than the other. Both half-shafts therefore rotate at the same speed as the crown wheel; the drive from the crown wheel to the half-shafts is transmitted through the bevel pinions, which drag the half-shaft bevels round but do not rotate on their own bearings. The advantage of the differential is that it permits one wheel to rotate faster than the other during cornering. This is made possible by the rotation of the bevel pinions on their own bearings; if one wheel starts to move faster than the crown wheel, it causes the bevel pinions to rotate on their

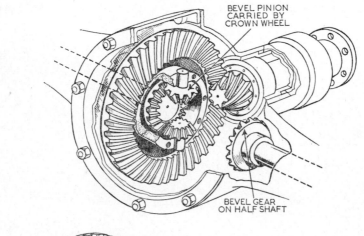

BEVEL PINION
CARRIED BY
CROWN WHEEL

BEVEL GEAR
ON HALF SHAFT

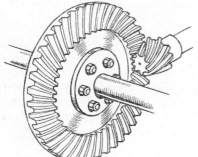

*Fig.* 12.11. *The rear axle differential. When the car is travelling in a straight line, the bevel pinions do not rotate on their shafts and both half shafts turn at the same speed as the crown wheel. When the car turns a corner, one rear wheel must rotate faster than the other and this " differential " rotation is permitted by rotation of the bevel pinions on their own shafts. If the half shafts were coupled rigidly to the crown wheel as on the left, no differential motion would be possible*

bearings and they in turn cause the other wheel to move more *slowly* than the crown wheel. Suppose, for example, that the crown wheel is being driven by the propeller-shaft pinion at 300 r.p.m.; then, if one wheel speeds up to 320 r.p.m. on a corner, the other automatically slows down to 280 r.p.m. The crown wheel always rotates at the *average* of the two wheel speeds.

The differential movement can be observed clearly when the back wheels of a car are jacked up. If the engine is locked in gear so that the stiffness of the engine prevents the propeller shaft from rotating, then when one of the back wheels is turned, the other wheel turns in the *opposite* direction.

A slight disadvantage of the differential arises when one of the wheels loses its grip, as, for example, on muddy ground. The other wheel may have a perfectly good grip but the car is unable to move. The bevel gear on the shaft with the good grip remains stationary; as the crown wheel rotates, the differential pinions run round the stationary bevel and drive the shaft of the slipping wheel at twice the crown wheel speed. To get the car moving, the grip of the slipping wheel must be restored either by placing grit under it or wedging it in some way. To overcome this problem, " limited slip " differentials have been designed

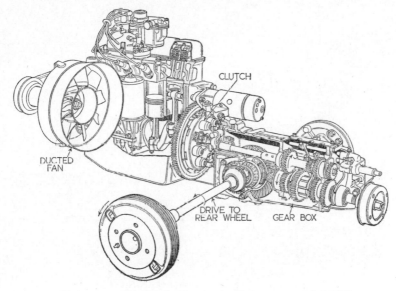

*Fig.* 12.12. *The Fiat 600 has its tiny 600 c.c. water-cooled OHV engine installed at the rear. The 4-speed gear box carries the pinion which engages with the crown wheel; it has no layshaft in the usual sense*

in which the relative speed between the half shafts is limited by a friction device.

### The Rear Engine

The practice of placing the engine at the *front* of the vehicle and then driving through the *back* wheels seems rather incongruous at first sight. The engine-in-front position is a tradition that can be traced back to the days of the horse and carriage. One alternative is to drive through the back wheels and also to locate the engine at the rear. The chief advantages that would accrue would be abolition of the propeller shaft and the possibility of a compact combined gear box and differential unit. Against this may be set the transfer of too much weight to the rear of the car, the greater difficulty of cooling the engine and the difficulty of providing adequate luggage accommodation under the bonnet.

Continental designers, however, are showing some preference for the rear engine on the smaller size of car. Examples of rear-engined cars

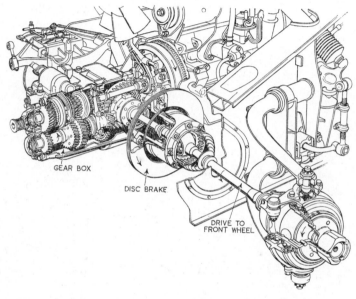

*Fig. 12.13. Citroën front engine and front wheel drive. The drive uses special " constant velocity " universal joints to permit the steering movement of the front wheels without fluctuation in rotational speed. Conventional springs are eliminated in the hydro-pneumatic suspension*

are the Renault Dauphine, the Fiat 600, the Volkswagen and the Chevrolet " Compact " car.

The engine installation of the Fiat 600 is illustrated in Fig. 12.12. The engine is one of the smallest 4-cylinder, water-cooled, overhead-valve engines in production. The radiator is placed at the side of the engine and is cooled by a high-efficiency ducted fan. Unlike a conventional gear box, the input and output shafts are at the same end. A rigid rear axle is unsuitable with a rear-engine installation, partly because there is no room for it and partly because the differential is attached to the gear box and cannot be allowed to move with the wheels. Independent rear-wheel suspension is therefore used and the two driving shafts have to be flexibly coupled to the differential unit; universal couplings are used for this purpose.

### Front-wheel Drive

A second alternative to the traditional engine-in-front and rear-wheel drive arrangement is to use front-wheel drive, keeping the engine in front. This form of transmission, the " traction avant ", was popularized by the French firm of Citroën in the 1930's and has been continued on their post-war cars (Fig. 12.13). As with the rear-engine arrangement, the abolition of the propeller shaft permits a low floor line un-

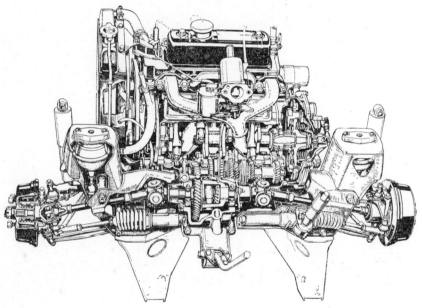

*Fig. 12.14. The B.M.C. baby cars use front-wheel drive with the engine mounted transversely. The engine is conventional but the sump is replaced by a large casting which houses the gear box and differential. The usual crown wheel and pinion are replaced by a pair of helical gears since no right-angled drive is required with a transverse engine*

obstructed by the usual shaft " tunnel ". A further advantage of front-wheel drive is the fact that the car is now pulled along instead of being pushed. Under most conditions the effect is a marked improvement in the responsiveness of the steering.

A certain difficulty arises in transmitting a front-wheel drive owing to the need to steer with the driving wheels. One solution is to use two universal joints of conventional design in each driving shaft. This arrangement is not altogether satisfactory, however, owing to the fact that an ordinary universal joint does not transmit constant speed. If the driving shaft runs at constant speed, the speed of the driven shaft is only constant when the two shafts are in line. When there is an angle between the shafts, the speed of the output shaft rises and falls alternately. With a conventional propeller shaft transmission, the fluctuation is negligible owing to the smallness of the angles between the shafts. In a front wheel drive, however, the angles may be quite large and the speed fluctuation appreciable. Special universal joints have been developed to overcome this difficulty. Joints of this type are used for the outer pair of couplings on the B.M.C. Austin 7 and Morris Miniminor (Fig. 12.14).

# Chapter 13

# TWO-PEDAL CONTROL

O NE of the greatest difficulties in learning to drive is the proper use of the clutch pedal when starting from rest and when changing gear. Whilst the experienced driver may take some pleasure in skilful use of the clutch and gear box, there must be many drivers besides learners who would not be sorry to see the clutch pedal disappear. Although two-pedal motoring (accelerator and brake) has long been a practical possibility, it is only in recent years that it has become available on popular cars as a moderately-priced optional extra. The driver still has to operate the gear lever but the clutch is operated for him automatically.

The description "two-pedal control" can reasonably be applied to any car on which the clutch pedal is unnecessary. It can therefore be applied both to fully automatic systems on which gear changing itself is automatic and to those semi-automatic systems on which the driver must operate the gear lever himself. However, in the present chapter, two-pedal control is taken to refer to semi-automatic systems only. As yet, these systems do not appear to have achieved very much popularity. It may well be that the majority of owners who are looking for easier driving will be prepared to pay rather more and have a fully automatic transmission (*see* next chapter).

### Automatic Clutch Operation

Two-pedal control is achieved by applying automatic clutch operation to an engine fitted with a conventional gear box. It must be emphasized that two-pedal control does not mean the abolition of the clutch but only of the clutch pedal. The basic principle of these systems is simple. As soon as the driver takes hold of the gear lever in order to make a change, an automatic control disengages the clutch. The power for operating the clutch can be supplied in various ways as described below. In effect, the slightest movement of the gear lever switches on the power supply and causes the clutch to be disengaged. Because of the simplicity of the system and the fact that a conventional gear box can be used two-pedal control is cheaper than fully automatic control; the latter normally requires a gear box and an engine coupling of special design (*see* Chapter 14).

### The Vacuum-operated Clutch

A convenient method of supplying the power for automatic clutch operation is to make use of the partial vacuum in the engine inlet manifold; the principle of operation is illustrated in Fig. 13.1. The

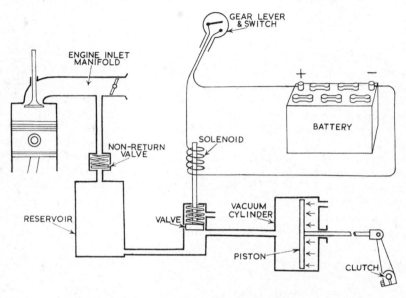

*Fig. 13.1. Power for automatic clutch operation can be obtained by making use of the partial vacuum in the engine inlet manifold. When the driver moves the gear lever, he closes a switch, thus energizing the solenoid and causing the left-hand side of the piston to be exposed to the partial vacuum in the reservoir*

clutch is disengaged by movement of the piston in the vacuum cylinder. One side of the piston is exposed to atmospheric pressure whilst the other is connected to the engine inlet manifold via the electrically operated valve and the reservoir.

Under certain running conditions, as for instance when the engine throttle valve is partially closed, the pressure in the engine inlet manifold is very much lower than atmospheric. Air flows from the reservoir into the manifold past the non-return valve thus reducing the pressure in the reservoir. If the throttle valve is opened and the manifold pressure rises, the non-return valve closes and prevents air from leaking back into the reservoir. Thus a partial vacuum is maintained continuously in the reservoir.

Except during gear changing, the switch in the gear lever is open and the electric coil or solenoid operating the valve is out of action. The plunger is therefore in its lowest position and the vacuum cylinder is exposed to atmospheric pressure via the vent. Both sides of the piston are therefore subject to atmospheric pressure and the clutch remains engaged. As soon as the driver grasps the gear lever, he automatically closes the switch. An electric current passes through the solenoid which then acts like a magnet in the manner described earlier in the discussion of ignition coils (Chapter 6). The iron plunger is drawn upwards, raising the valve and connecting the vacuum cylinder to reservoir. The force acting on the right-hand side of the piston is now higher than that acting on the left and the piston therefore moves to the left, exerting a pull on the rod and causing the clutch to be disengaged. As soon as the driver has changed gear and released the lever, the switch opens and the clutch is re-engaged.

Various refinements can be made for improving the performance. The Manumatic control system, for example, incorporates an automatic control for adjusting the engine speed during gear changing by regulating the throttle position; in this way, very smooth changes can be carried out swiftly and automatically. The vacuum piston rod can be hydraulically connected to the clutch withdrawal lever, so allowing the designer greater freedom in locating the vacuum cylinder.

**The Centrifugal Clutch**

The vacuum system just described could be used in conjunction with a conventional clutch of the type described in Chapter 10. Some systems, however, incorporate centrifugal clutches of special design. The advantage of these clutches is that they disengage automatically when the speed of the engine falls below a certain value. Thus the car can be brought to rest in any gear without stalling the engine. Similarly, any gear can be engaged with the car at rest and left in position, but the clutch does not become engaged until the driver depresses the accelerator and revs up the engine. All the driver has to do to start, after selecting a gear, is to release the brakes and put his foot on the accelerator. These two features are particularly helpful to the learner driver.

The method of operation of the Newton centrifugal clutch is illustrated in Fig. 13.2. Three bob weights are attached to levers which are located on pivots and rotate with the engine flywheel. As the engine speed increases, the bob weights are flung outwards and the ends of the levers press against the springs so that the friction disc is gripped between the flywheel and the pressure plate in the usual way. The bob weights fit into holes in the flywheel and the outer part of the flywheel prevents the weights from flying out too far. Thus the force on the clutch friction plate does not increase indefinitely but remains constant above a certain engine speed. When the engine speed is low, the springs are able to expand and the bob weights come up against the inner edge of the holes. The backs of the levers press against the nuts on the studs; these studs are attached to the pressure plate and in this way the plate is

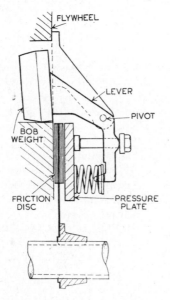

*Fig.* 13.2. *Newton centrifugal clutch (half-section). Three bob weights (only one is shown) are attached to levers and rotate with the engine flywheel. When the engine speed rises, the bob weights are flung out by centrifugal force. The pressure plate is forced to the left and the friction disc is gripped between the plate and the flywheel*

withdrawn and the clutch disengaged. Disengagement of the clutch by the clutch pedal can be effected in the normal way.

### The Magnetic Clutch

Another method of achieving two-pedal control is by using a magnetically operated clutch instead of the vacuum-operated type described above. This is the principle of the Ferlec clutch used on some Renault cars. The method of operation is illustrated in the simplified diagram shown in Fig. 13.3. The friction disc D is splined to the output shaft in the usual way and when the clutch is disengaged it is free to rotate between the pressure plate P and the flywheel plate N. The plate N is bolted rigidly to the flywheel whilst the plate P is bolted to the armature plate A. The latter plate is lightly attached to the flywheel by three spring links as shown in an inset diagram in Fig. 13.3; thus the plates A and P are obliged to rotate with the flywheel but the gap S is variable owing to the flexibility of the spring links. The engine flywheel has a large circular groove cut in the right-hand face and this groove houses a coil of wire which can be fed with current from the battery. When current is flowing, the coil acts as a magnet and attracts the iron armature plate A towards it. The pressure plate is drawn in the same direction and the friction plate becomes gripped between the pressure plate P and the flywheel plate N; both of these plates are rotating with the flywheel and the drive is therefore transmitted by friction as with a conventional clutch.

When the driver grasps the gear lever to change gear, he opens a switch in the lever and causes a break in the current to the electro-magnet; the grip on the friction disc is relaxed and the clutch becomes disengaged. In normal operation, the coil is connected to the engine dynamo and not to the battery. When, therefore, the engine speed and the dynamo output fall to a low value the clutch is automatically disengaged (three light coil springs, not shown, are carried in the flywheel; these press against the armature plate and overcome the

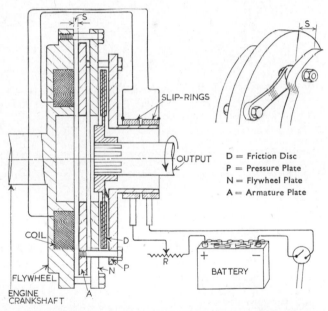

*Fig. 13.3. Principle of the Ferlac magnetic clutch used by Renault. The pressure plate P is secured to the armature plate A and both are carried on the flywheel by means of spring links (see inset drawing). When current is flowing in the coil, it produces a magnetic force which attracts the armature plate to the left. The friction disc D is thus gripped between the flywheel plate N and the pressure plate P. When the driver grasps the gear lever, he opens a switch which interrupts the current in the coil, thus disengaging the clutch*

149

magnetic force when it is low). The effect of this feature is similar to that of a centrifugal clutch—the car can be brought to rest in gear without danger of stalling. Progressive engagement of the clutch during starting is achieved by means of the variable electrical resistance R which is controlled by movement of the accelerator pedal. As the pedal is depressed, the resistance is gradually cut out; the current in the coil and the pressure on the friction plate therefore increase progressively.

The powder-gap magnetic clutch works on a somewhat different principle. The drive from the flywheel to the gear-box input shaft is

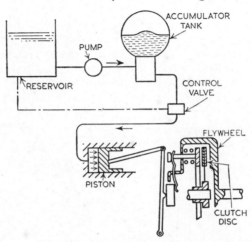

*Fig.* 13.4. *Hydraulic clutch operation (Citroën). The conventional friction clutch is disengaged by means of oil pressure, generated by an engine-driven pump. When the driver moves the gear lever, an electric switch is operated, causing the control valve to open; oil is allowed to flow from the accumulator tank and the pressure causes the piston to move to the right*

transmitted through a film of magnetized iron powder. The powder is contained in a gap formed between the inside of a cylindrical cavity in the flywheel and the outside of a thick disc which drives the gear-box input shaft. The magnetic force is provided by the current in a coil which is adjacent to the powder gap. During changes of gear, this current is automatically interrupted by a switch in the gear lever.

### Hydraulic Clutch Operation

Two-pedal control can also be achieved by operating the clutch hydraulically as is done on the Citroën 2-litre. We must make a clear distinction here between hydraulic *control* and hydraulic *operation*. " Hydraulic control " is the term that was used to describe the replacement of the mechanical link between the clutch pedal and the clutch operating lever by a hydraulic link (*see* Chapter 10). When we use the term " hydraulic operation " we mean that the *power* for operating the clutch is supplied hydraulically from a pressurised oil system (instead of by pressure of the driver's foot or other means).

As with the vacuum-operated system described earlier, a conventional clutch of the type described in Chapter 10 is used. The operating force, however, is supplied by the pressure of oil acting on a piston (*see* Fig. 13.4). The hydraulic pressure is supplied from a special pump which is driven by the engine. The pump draws its supply from a reservoir and maintains a high pressure in an accumulator tank; oil for operating the clutch is drawn from this tank and led to the hydraulic cylinder via a control valve (the tank can also be used to supply hydraulic power for other purposes). The control valve is electrically controlled by a switch in the gear changing lever. When the lever is grasped, the control valve opens and admits oil to the hydraulic cylinder; the clutch is thus automatically disengaged.

# Chapter 14

## AUTOMATIC TRANSMISSION

A FULLY automatic transmission is one that completely relieves the driver from the duty of changing gear. Having moved a lever to select either " forward " or " reverse ", he has only to press the accelerator and the car will accelerate to the required speed; when the accelerator is released and the brake applied, the car comes to a standstill and the engine continues to tick over quietly. It would be quite possible to apply an automatic control system to a car fitted with a conventional clutch and gear box; the vacuum-operated clutch described in the last chapter represents a step in this direction. However, experience has shown that fully automatic transmission is more satisfactory when the transmission has been specially designed for that purpose. Most of the automatic transmissions used in Britain and America are based upon a fluid torque converter or a fluid coupling working in conjunction with an epicyclic gear box. The present chapter deals mainly with the operating principles of these three components. Because of the complexity of design of most automatic transmissions, it has been found necessary to leave aside details of mechanical construction in order to concentrate on the essential features. The Smiths automatic transmission, described at the end of the chapter, is a more recent development and consists basically of an electro-magnetic clutch and an electrically operated gear box.

### The Fluid Coupling

A fluid coupling is not in itself an automatic transmission. It is really a kind of automatic clutch which transmits power from one shaft to another by means of the circulation of oil between the two halves of the coupling. Alternative names for it are " hydraulic coupling " and " fluid flywheel ". The latter name is, of course, only appropriate when the coupling is incorporated in the engine flywheel as it is on the Daimler preselector transmission. A fluid coupling is also used on the General Motors " Hydramatic " automatic transmission. The coupling has two main parts—an impeller wheel, made in two halves and forming a drum, and an output wheel (Fig. 14.1). The impeller wheel or drum is attached to the driving shaft and has a number of radial vanes attached to one of its inner faces. The output wheel is located inside the drum and is also provided with vanes which face those on the drum. The impeller wheel is oil-tight and is filled with oil.

If the car is at rest and the output shaft is stationary, the impeller drum rotates with the crankshaft and, provided the engine speed is low, the churning of the oil is insufficient to cause much drag on the engine. In effect, the " clutch " is disengaged. When, however, the engine is accelerated, the impeller vanes tend to fling the oil outwards and create a high oil pressure at the outside. As the output wheel is either stationary or rotating at a lower speed than the impeller, the oil pressure between the output vanes is comparatively low; oil therefore flows towards the output wheel at the outside and then recirculates through the impeller vanes. As the oil has a high rotational speed when it enters the output

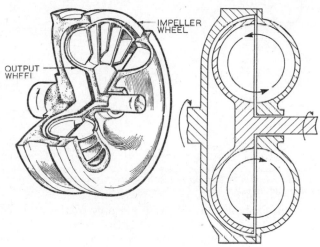

*Fig. 14.1. A fluid coupling. The impeller wheel is driven by the engine, whilst the output wheel is coupled to the gear box. Torque is transmitted by means of the circulation of oil between the vanes attached to the two wheels. The input and output torques are equal*

wheel, it tends to drag the latter round with it and in this way torque is transferred from one half of the coupling to the other.

The torque exerted by the impeller drum on the output wheel is, of course, equal to the resisting torque exerted by the wheel on the drum. (Just as the pull exerted by a horse on a cart equals the drag of the cart on the horse.) The input and output torques of a fluid coupling are therefore equal. The output *speed* on the other hand, assuming that the engine is transmitting power, is always less than the input speed; if it were not, the output wheel would be rotating as fast as the oil flung into it and there could be no transfer of torque. This difference in speed means that there is a loss of power, and the greater the difference the greater the loss. If the engine input shaft is rotating at 3,000 r.p.m. say, and the output shaft to the gear box is only turning at 1,000 r.p.m., the power loss may be as much as 70 per cent of the input. If, however, a lower gear is engaged so that, with the car travelling at the same speed

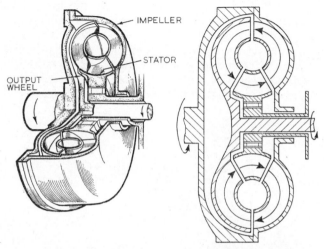

Fig. 14.2. *A fluid torque converter. The impeller is driven by the engine, whilst the output wheel is coupled to the gearing. The stator does not rotate. The presence of the stator reduces the drag exerted by the output wheel on the impeller so that the output torque exceeds the input torque; but the output speed is correspondingly less than the input speed*

as before, the output shaft from the coupling now rotates at 2,900 r.p.m., the loss may be as low as 3 per cent. It is therefore essential for a fluid coupling to be properly matched to the engine and gear box if reasonable fuel consumption is to be secured.

### The Fluid Torque Converter

When an engine is developing a certain power, we can either engage a high gear and get a moderate torque (turning effort) in the propeller shaft at high shaft speed, or we can engage a low gear and get a high torque at a low speed of the propeller shaft. The engine speed and torque are assumed to be the same in both cases. As the gears are changed from high to low, the torque in the propeller shaft is stepped up in a series of jumps. A torque converter is designed to do a similar job but to do it smoothly and automatically. When the car encounters a gradient and the speed of the car and that of the propeller shaft fall, the torque output from the converter increases although the engine speed and throttle opening remain constant.   If this torque conversion could take place over the whole speed range of the car without loss of power, we would have the perfect transmission and no gear changes would be required.   Unfortunately a fluid torque converter is only efficient over a restricted range of speed and it must usually be combined with a gear box having at least two gear ratios.   Nevertheless, the amount of gear changing required is less than with a conventional transmission and it is easier to achieve automatic operation.

The fluid torque converter bears a resemblance to a fluid coupling (Fig. 14.2).   The principal differences are that curved vanes are used and that as the oil returns from the output wheel to the impeller wheel it passes through a stator, that is a ring of stationary blades.   It is the presence of the stator that enables the torque increase to take place; without the stator, the converter would simply behave as a fluid coupling, the input and output torques being equal.   The difference between a fluid coupling and a torque converter may perhaps be clarified by referring to Fig. 14.3.   The upper diagram shows iron balls being passed between two moving belts.   One belt is moving faster than the other and corresponds to the impeller wheel of a fluid coupling; the other belt corresponds to the output wheel.   The transfer of the iron balls corresponds to the flow of oil.   As the balls from the input belt chute fall into the compartments on the output belt, a series of impulses is given to the output belt causing it to be driven along with a certain force.   Similarly, when the balls are returned to the input belt they cause a drag on it since the output belt is moving more slowly.   The force required to move the input belt will be equal to the force exerted by the balls on the output belt.   The effect would be the same if the balls were replaced by buckets of water or jets from hoses; thus the moving belts are similar in action to a fluid coupling.

The arrangement, shown in the lower half of the diagram, is equivalent to a fluid torque converter.   Just as curved blades and a stator are used to obtain torque conversion, so an inclined chute and a stator chute are used to obtain an increase in force on the output belt.   The balls leaving the output belt are directed to the rear; as they roll down the chute, they are pushing in the direction of rotation and increasing the force propelling the output belt.   Now if the balls were directed straight on to the impeller belt, they would increase the drag on this belt by an equal amount and the input and output forces would still be equal. The function of the stator is to reduce the tangential velocity of the balls so that the force on the impeller belt is unchanged.   The output force is therefore greater than the input force.   When the speed of the

155

output belt is close to that of the impeller belt, the force imparted to the output belt by the balls arriving from the impeller belt will not be very great. When, however, the speed of the output belt is low, the impulse received from the balls is much greater. Thus the driving force increases as the output belt speed is reduced, just as the torque from a converter increases as the output-shaft speed falls.

The basic "three-element" type of torque converter described here has been used on several automatic transmissions including the Borg-Warner transmission fitted to many British cars. Other more complex

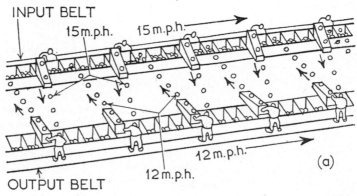

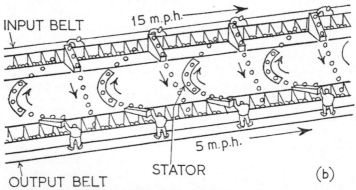

Fig. 14.3. (a) The transfer of the balls between the input and output belts is similar to the transfer of oil between the impeller and output wheels of a fluid coupling. The impulse given to the output belt by the balls from the input belt equals the drag on the input belt exerted by the balls when they arrive back.

(b) This arrangement corresponds to the action of a fluid torque converter. The balls are directed backwards from the output belt, so increasing the force on the output belt by reaction. The stator, however, directs the balls forward on to the input belt, so reducing the drag exerted on the input belt. Thus the output force exceeds the input force

torque converters are in use in which some or all of the impeller and output wheels and the stator are split into separate stages in order to give improved efficiency over a wide range of speed. Sometimes the angle of the stator vanes is variable, as on the Buick " Dynaflow " transmission. Owing to the large power loss that occurs under certain conditions, all torque converters require some form of cooling. In top gear, it is usually arranged for an automatically operated clutch to lock

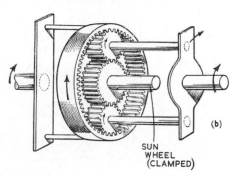

*Fig. 14.4. An epicyclic gear train of the type used in many automatic gear boxes. The ring wheel is driven by the engine. (a) With the carrier clamped, the output comes from the sun wheel and the unit acts like a normal gear train. (b) Usually, however, the sun wheel is clamped and the drive is taken from the carrier. The planets rotate " epicyclically " around the sun wheel*

the input and output sides of the torque converter together, so increasing top-gear economy.

Torque converters are unsuitable for small engines since, if the diameter of the impeller is much reduced in size, the fluid velocity becomes too low for effective operation. Consequently, the unit would have to be disproportionately large on a small engine.

**Epicyclic Gearing**

Most fully automatic transmissions make use of epicyclic gearing which lends itself to smooth and automatic gear changing. Before discussing the epicyclic principle it will be helpful to refer to Fig. 14.4(a). In this diagram, the ring wheel drives the sun wheel through a pair of planet wheels which are mounted on a carrier. Provided the carrier is held stationary, the gearing can be regarded in the normal way. If, for example, the ring wheel has 40 teeth and the sun wheel 20 teeth, then when the ring wheel turns at 1,000 r.p.m., the sun wheel turns at 2,000 r.p.m. in the reverse direction. If, however, we clamp the sun wheel in position and allow the *carrier* to be driven, we convert the gears into an epicyclic unit (Fig. 14.4(b) ). The essential difference is that the centres of some of the gears, namely the planet gears, are no longer fixed; with normal gearing, all gear centres remain fixed.

When the ring wheel is turned with the sun wheel held stationary, the planet wheels are obliged to " run around " the sun wheel and they take the carrier round with them. The carrier rotates in the same direction as the input shaft but at a reduced speed. If the ring and sun gears have 40 and 20 teeth respectively as before, then when the input shaft rotates at 3,000 r.p.m., the output shaft rotates at 2,000 r.p.m. (The process is less easy to visualize than with normal gearing, but the actual calculation is not particularly difficult.)

Other types of epicyclic gear train exist, but the type shown in Fig. 14.4(b) is very common and is used in many automatic transmissions including the Borg-Warner and the Hydramatic.

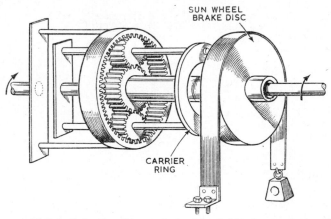

*Fig. 14.5. Method of clamping the sun wheel. The shafting is rearranged so that the carrier output shaft passes through a hollow sun wheel shaft to which the sun wheel brake disc is attached. No drive can be transmitted until the brake is applied. If the carrier ring and sun wheel brake disc are locked together by means of a clutch, the whole gear train is locked and a straight through drive is obtained*

The way in which the sun wheel can be clamped is shown diagrammatically in Fig. 14.5. A brake band passes over a disc which is integral with the sun wheel. It will be seen that the drive from the carrier has to be taken through the middle of the sun wheel in order to accommodate the brake band and disc. The advantage of epicyclic gearing should be clear from this diagram. The gears are constantly in mesh and it is only necessary to apply a load to the brake band in order to bring the gear train into operation. Direct drive between the input and output shafts can be obtained by relaxing the brake and locking the sun wheel to the carrier. With the arrangement shown in Fig. 14.5, this can be achieved by bringing the carrier ring into frictional contact with the sun brake disc. The whole gear train is thus locked together and rotates as a solid mass.

Epicyclic units of this sort are often combined with one or more similar units in order to provide a number of alternative gear ratios. On the Borg-Warner automatic transmission, the ring gear of the first

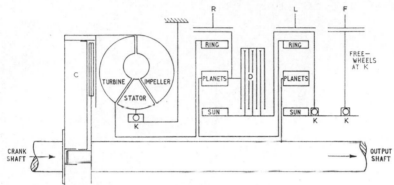

*Fig. 14.6. Diagram showing the layout of the Borg-Warner automatic transmission. For low gear, brakes F and L are applied; for intermediate gear, brake F and clutch D; for top gear, clutch C engages direct drive; and for reverse, brake R is applied*

gear train is driven by the output wheel of the torque converter. The drive from the planet carrier is then taken to the ring gear of a second epicyclic unit so that the two units act in series (*see* Fig. 14.6). This diagram is taken from a useful series of articles on Automatic Transmissions by R. F. Ansdale. The first article appeared in *The Autocar*, November 6th, 1959. On the General Motors " Hydramatic " transmission, the ring gear of the first unit is driven directly from the engine and the output from the carrier is taken to the input wheel of a fluid coupling. The output wheel of the coupling transmits the drive through further epicyclic gearing.

It is interesting to note that the epicyclic arrangement shown in Fig. 14.4(b) is similar to that used in the overdrive described in Chapter 11; the principal difference is that the input and output shafts are reversed.

### Automatic Control

A suitable combination of epicyclic gearing with a fluid coupling or a fluid torque converter does not in itself give automatic control. It

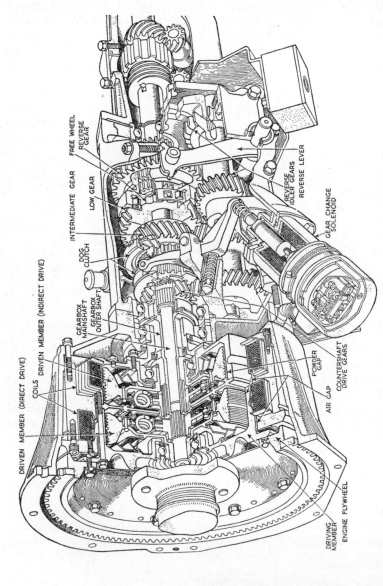

DRIVEN MEMBER (DIRECT DRIVE)

COILS

DRIVEN MEMBER (INDIRECT DRIVE)

GEARBOX MAINSHAFT

GEARBOX OUTER SHAFT

DOG CLUTCH

LOW GEAR

INTERMEDIATE GEAR

FREE WHEEL GEAR

REVERSE GEAR

REVERSE IDLER GEARS

REVERSE LEVER

GEAR CHANGE SOLENOID

POWDER GAP

COUNTERSHAFT DRIVE GEARS

AIR GAP

DRIVING MEMBER

ENGINE FLYWHEEL

*Fig.* 14.7(a). *Smiths "Easidrive" automatic transmission as used on the Hillman Minx. The change from low to intermediate gear is made when the solenoid operates the dog clutch; in intermediate gear, the low gear free-wheels. Reverse gear is obtained manually. (See also Fig.* 14.7(b) *opposite)*

simply provides a transmission to which automatic control can be applied with reasonable ease. Operation of the brake bands and internal clutches can be carried out hydraulically and the hydraulic pressure can be automatically regulated by a control unit which is sensitive to accelerator movement and to the speed of the car. With the Borg-Warner automatic transmission which is used on several British cars, the driver places a lever in one of five positions. For normal driving, the lever is set to D (Drive) and control is then fully automatic; the transmission automatically operates in the correct gear depending

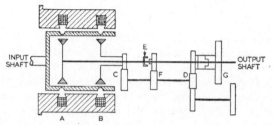

*Fig.* 14.7(*b*). *Smiths "Easidrive" automatic transmission. In low gear, clutch B is energized and the drive is transmitted through the gear pairs C and D. For intermediate gear, a solenoid engages the dog E; the drive is then through clutch B and the gear pairs C and F, with the pair D free-wheeling. Direct drive is obtained when clutch A is energized and clutch B is cut out. For reverse, gear pair G is engaged manually and clutch B is energized*

on the accelerator position and the speed of the car. If the driver wishes to hold the transmission in low gear, on a steep hill perhaps, he can select L (Low) and override the automatic change. The other positions are R (Reverse), P (Park) and N (Neutral). In the P position, the transmission is locked and the car cannot move. In the N position, the car is free to move but no drive is transmitted.

### Smiths Automatic Transmission

The Smiths automatic transmission differs radically from the type described earlier in the chapter in that it makes use neither of a fluid drive nor of epicyclic gearing. It is essentially a 3-speed gear box controlled by a pair of electromagnetic clutches and an electrically-operated gear-changing solenoid (Fig. 14.7 (a) and (b)). The clutches are of the magnetic powder-gap type; the drive to each clutch from the flywheel is transmitted through a small gap containing iron particles. These particles can only transmit torque when they are magnetized by a current in the surrounding coil which is stationary. The right-hand clutch is used for low and intermediate gears and the left-hand clutch for top gear (direct drive). Low gear is continuously engaged but contains a free wheel so that when the solenoid operates the sliding dog and engages intermediate gear, the low gear on the gear-box output shaft free-wheels. Reverse gear is engaged manually.

161

# Chapter 15

---

# ALTERNATIVES TO THE PETROL ENGINE

NEARLY all present-day motor cars are driven by petrol engines for the simple reason that no more generally satisfactory engine can be designed in the present state of engineering knowledge. Nevertheless, other types of engine had their day in the past and it is quite possible that other types will have their day in the future. In the present chapter we shall discuss the pros and cons of the following alternatives:

The Diesel Engine
The Gas Turbine
The Free Piston Engine
The Gas Engine
The Electric Car
The Steam Car
The Atomic Car.

Of these, only the diesel engine is used to any appreciable extent, though the gas turbine is being steadily developed and could one day become a serious competitor. The others are unlikely to be of much use in motor cars in the foreseeable future, for reasons which we shall try to explain.

### The Diesel Engine

The main advantage of the diesel engine compared with the petrol engine is its very much lower fuel consumption. Unfortunately, the diesel engine is considerably heavier and more costly, so that its main application to motor vehicles has been in the commercial field, where high mileage makes low fuel consumption particularly desirable.

From about 1930 the diesel engine has been gradually displacing the petrol engine in heavy commercial vehicles in this country, and its use has spread to medium-weight trucks and vans and to buses and motor coaches. Meanwhile the possibility of its application to taxicabs and private cars has not been overlooked, and efforts have been made to develop a lightweight engine for use in these fields. The diesel engine is well suited to taxicab operation and in the London area it is rapidly ousting the petrol engine. Although several diesel-powered cars are on the market, the rate of progress in this field is much slower for reasons discussed further on.

The engine owes its name to the German engineer Rudolf Diesel, who demonstrated his engine as long ago as 1898. Since then many developments have taken place and the modern diesel engine does not really function in the manner envisaged by Diesel. Many people prefer to use the descriptions " oil engine " or " compression-ignition engine ", but the term " diesel engine " is more common.

The diesel engine is very similar to the petrol engine both in construction and in operation. The similarity is so great that certain manufacturers make an engine which can easily be modified for use as a petrol or diesel engine, many components such as crankshaft and cylinder block being almost identical. In the 4-stroke diesel cycle, air is drawn into the cylinder during the suction stroke, but there is no

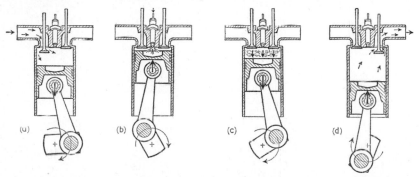

Fig. 15.1. *A diesel engine differs from a petrol engine in that the fuel is injected into the cylinder at the end of the compression stroke. No carburettor or ignition equipment is used*

(*a*) *Induction on suction stroke: inlet valve open; pure air enters cylinder as piston descends. Inlet valve closes at end of stroke*

(*b*) *Compression stroke: both valves closed; piston rises so compressing air. Fuel is injected near end of stroke and starts to burn owing to the high temperature and pressure*

(*c*) *Expansion stroke: pressure and temperature rise rapidly early in stroke and then fall as piston is forced downwards; power is transmitted to the crankshaft. Exhaust valve opens at end of stroke*

(*d*) *Exhaust stroke: exhaust valve opens; piston rises so expelling burnt gases from cylinder. At end of stroke, exhaust valve closes and inlet opens*

carburettor and only pure air enters the cylinder (*see* Fig. 15.1). On the second stroke the piston rises, compressing the air and causing its pressure and temperature to rise to high values. A fuel injector is mounted in the cylinder head in a similar position to the sparking plug of a petrol engine. The injector is supplied with fuel from a special high pressure pump and the design is such that the fuel required is injected in a fine spray towards the end of the compression stroke. As there is no sparking plug, combustion can only occur as the result of a high compression temperature; consequently the air has to be compressed much more than in a petrol engine—compression ratios between 15/1 and 20/1 are used in diesel engines compared with about 8/1 in overhead-valve petrol engines. There is a slight delay before combustion takes place, since the fuel droplets have to be heated by the air and a chemical reaction initiated. For this reason, injection is timed to begin just before the piston reaches the top of the cylinder, so that combustion will be in full progress when the expansion stroke commences. Fuel injection and combustion continue into the early part of the expansion stroke in contrast to the petrol engine, where combustion is normally completed more quickly. At the end of the expansion stroke, the exhaust valve opens and in the following stroke the exhaust gases are forced from the cylinder. As the piston reaches the top of the cylinder the exhaust valve closes and the inlet valve opens ready for the second

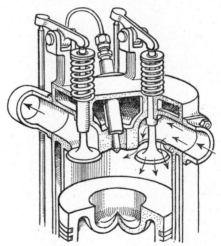

*Fig. 15.2. A direct ignition diesel engine. The fuel is injected into a cavity in the piston crown*

cycle. The valve gear therefore operates in the same way as in the petrol engine.

Although the diesel engine is similar in construction to a petrol engine, its combustion process and fuel system are quite different. In the petrol engine, by the time the spark occurs the petrol is in the form of vapour, and is completely mixed with the air so that the flame spreads through a uniform mixture. But in the diesel engine, the fuel only enters the cylinder at the last moment and is in the form of liquid droplets. To ensure that combustion is completed early in the expansion stroke, two conditions must be satisfied:

1. The fuel injected must be broken up into a finely atomized spray of tiny droplets.
2. The air in the cylinder must be in violent motion so that all the droplets come into contact with the available oxygen and none are stifled in the burnt gas from other droplets.

The first aim is achieved by injecting the fuel at very high pressure through an injector nozzle containing one or more small holes. The

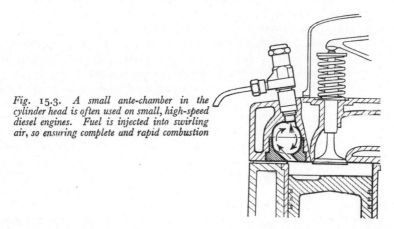

*Fig. 15.3. A small ante-chamber in the cylinder head is often used on small, high-speed diesel engines. Fuel is injected into swirling air, so ensuring complete and rapid combustion*

injector is connected to the fuel pump through a steel tube, and receives a charge of fuel for every two turns of the crankshaft. A valve in the centre of the injector seals off the nozzle holes to prevent " dribbling " and only opens when the pump pressure rises at the beginning of fuel injection. The fuel pump consists of a cylinder containing a sliding piston or plunger which is operated by a rotating cam. On multi-cylinder engines, the pump embodies a separate cam and plunger for each engine cylinder. The new distributor-type pumps, however, use a single pump of special design to supply fuel to each engine cylinder in turn through a rotating " distributor ". On both types, the pump is driven from the engine crankshaft at half engine speed. The fuel delivered by the pump is controlled by the movement of the accelerator pedal; thus the engine power of a diesel engine is varied by altering the amount of fuel injected. In contrast to this, the throttle valve on the petrol-engine carburettor varies the amount of mixture, i.e. of fuel *and* air.

The second aim, ensuring violent motion of the air, can be achieved in several ways. In the engine illustrated in Fig. 15.2, fuel is injected directly into the cylinder, hence the term " direct injection ". The top face of the piston comes very close to the cylinder head at the end of compression so that most of the air is squeezed into the recess in the crown of the piston. The resulting air motion is sufficiently violent to ensure thorough mixing when the fuel spray is directed into this space. This type of design is popular on the larger British engines. A Ricardo type of ante-chamber design similar to the one shown in Fig. 15.3 is often employed on the small high speed engines used in motor cars. The cylinder head contains a small space known as the ante-chamber, into which most of the air is forced at the end of compression. The fuel is injected into the ante-chamber and when combustion begins the pressure in the ante-chamber rises, causing a mixture of air and fuel to be ejected through the connecting hole into the main cylinder. The high ejection velocity ensures the rapid mixing of fuel droplets and air which is essential to efficient diesel-engine operation.

Diesel oil contains roughly the same proportion of hydrogen and carbon as petrol, but the two elements are combined in a different form so that the physical properties of diesel oil are rather different from those of petrol. Diesel oil is rather heavier than petrol—a gallon of diesel oil weighs about 18 per cent more than a gallon of petrol, and it contains correspondingly more energy. A gallon of diesel oil costs about the same as a gallon of petrol, so that the cost of diesel-oil energy is rather less than that of petrol energy. Added to this, the high compression ratio of the diesel engine results in higher efficiency —a diesel engine gives more power than a petrol engine for the same consumption of fuel energy. Also, reducing the throttle opening on a petrol engine reduces the compression pressure and hence reduces part load efficiency. Finally, the diesel fuel pump is a more precise instrument for delivering fuel to the cylinders than the petrol-engine carburettor. All these factors combine to make the fuel cost per mile for a diesel engine little more than half of that of the corresponding petrol engine.

But the diesel engine has certain disadvantages which have prevented its wide application to motor cars. The high cylinder pressures resulting from high compression ratios lead to a more robust design and greater engine weight. But apart from this effect, which is tending to become small in modern designs, a diesel engine has to be bulkier than a petrol engine of the same power, for two reasons. Firstly, because of the difficulty in getting thorough mixing of the fuel and air, about 20 per cent more air than is theoretically required for complete combustion has to be drawn into the cylinder. Without this excess air, many fuel droplets would fail to find the oxygen required and the result would be a very smoky exhaust. No power is derived from this excess air, although the engine cylinder has to be large enough to accommodate it. The second reason is the slower speed at which a diesel engine can operate efficiently. The time available for fuel injection and combustion is extremely short—about $\frac{1}{200}$ sec at 3,000 r.p.m.—and there is great difficulty in designing fuel pumps and injector nozzles that can operate at appreciably greater speeds. The quantity of fuel injected into each cylinder in each cycle is very small and the pump and injectors have to be very accurately manufactured if they are to deliver the precise quantity at the instant required. The petrol engine, on the other hand, can easily operate at 5,000 r.p.m. and delivers correspondingly more power for the same size of engine.

At present the diesel engine costs £100 or so more than the corresponding petrol engine, and it requires some 30,000 miles of motoring before the saving in fuel cost offsets the higher initial cost. In actual performance, acceleration and smoothness, the diesel engine at its best can hardly hope to equal the petrol engine, let alone surpass it. Until a cheap, reliable high-speed fuel system can be produced, the diesel engine is unlikely to make much progress in displacing the petrol engine from its dominant position in the field of private motoring.

### The Gas Turbine

Ever since the gas-turbine jet engine made its dramatic impact on the aircraft industry and began to oust the petrol engine from its hitherto unchallenged position, motor manufacturers in Britain, Europe and America have felt obliged to consider the chances of a successful application of the gas turbine to motor cars and commercial vehicles. One of the reasons for the success of the gas turbine in the air was its ability to deliver much more power than a petrol engine of the same weight. Low weight also is an attraction for the automobile designer, since he is anxious to reduce the dead weight that has to be carried up and down hills, accelerated and brought to rest by braking. Another attraction of the gas turbine is its purely rotary motion—there is no piston or crankshaft mechanism to cause vibration and wear. Following the public demonstration of the Rover gas turbine car in 1950, several manufacturers have announced their development of gas-turbine engines for automobile use and have carried out road tests in private cars and in trucks.

Before outlining the principle of the automobile gas turbine, two points should be made clear. Firstly, the description " gas " turbine simply distinguishes the engine from the steam turbine and does not refer to the fuel used. Whilst a gas turbine can be made to run on gas, only liquid fuels such as paraffin, petrol and diesel oil are likely to be considered for road use. Secondly, the gas turbine as used for road vehicles is not a jet engine. In the aircraft gas-turbine jet engine, all the power is used in producing a high velocity jet of hot gases to propel the aircraft by reaction, but this principle is never likely to commend itself to automobile designers. In the automobile gas turbine, the velocity of the jet, i.e. the velocity of the gases leaving the exhaust pipe, must be reduced to a minimum, partly to avoid nuisance to other road users and partly to ensure that all the available power is transferred to the driving shaft.

The essential principle of the gas turbine can be explained by reference to Fig. 15.4. A single shaft carrying an air compressor and a turbine

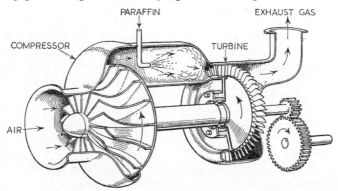

*Fig. 15.4. A simple gas turbine. A single turbine drives both the compressor and the output shaft*

rotates at high speed in ball or roller bearings. The air compressor operates by centrifugal action: air is drawn from the atmosphere into the eye of the compressor and is given a rotary motion by the vanes cut in the side of a rotating disc or impeller. The air is flung out radially at high speed and at increased pressure and then enters a collector or diffuser which is a diverging passage in which the velocity of the air is reduced whilst its pressure is further increased. The compressed air now enters the combustion chamber where a fuel nozzle delivers a continuous spray of fuel under pressure from a fuel pump. Once the spray has been ignited by an electric spark, combustion is continuous and no further ignition is required. The hot gases from the combustion chamber are led through ducting to a ring of turbine nozzles. These nozzles direct the hot gases at high velocity on to the turbine rotor blades, the pressure of the gases falling through the nozzles as their velocity increases. The turbine blades are shaped so as to catch the hot gases and bend them round in the opposite direction. The gases thus exert a turning force on the turbine rotor and leave the rotor with most of their energy expended, after which they escape to the atmosphere through the exhaust duct. This turning force is greater than the torque required to drive the compressor and the difference is available for driving the power shaft through the reduction gear.

The turbine shaft has to rotate at high speed, 25,000 r.p.m. or more, in order that the centrifugal action of the impeller should be sufficient to raise the air pressure to the required value. The reduction gear is necessary in order to reduce the speed of the power shaft to a reasonably low value comparable with the speed of a petrol engine crankshaft.

The gas turbine is smooth and continuous in action. There is no sequence of compression, explosion and expansion as in the petrol engine; compression, combustion and expansion all take place smoothly and simultaneously. No flywheel is required as the turbine exerts a smooth and continuous torque on the shaft. Reciprocating motion, which leads to vibration, wear and noise, is completely absent. The number of parts, and particularly the number of moving parts and bearings, is very much smaller than for a petrol engine. Valves, camshafts, ignition-timing devices, and above all, the crankshaft, have disappeared, leaving the engineer's dream—a pure rotary motion.

The above description, however, has reduced the gas turbine to its bare essentials. It is also necessary to provide a fuel pump driven from the main shaft in order to supply the combustion chamber with fuel at high pressure. A starter motor must also be geared to the main shaft and must be capable of taking the engine up to a comparatively high speed, probably 10,000 r.p.m. or so, before the turbine becomes self-sustaining. A further modification to the simple picture presented above concerns the coupling of the power shaft to the vehicle. Clearly a direct coupling cannot be used, since it would be impossible for the turbine shaft to turn with the vehicle at rest; power would only be developed when the vehicle had reached a considerable speed. It would be possible to use a clutch and gear box in the usual way, but the gas turbine offers a cheaper and more attractive alternative. Instead of gearing the main compressor shaft to the power shaft, the main shaft is allowed to run freely and the main-shaft turbine is designed to extract just sufficient power from the gases to drive the compressor—it is then called the compressor turbine. A similar turbine, mounted on a separate shaft and geared to the power shaft, is placed downstream of the compressor turbine with a second ring of nozzles between them to direct the gases on to the second or power turbine, as shown in Fig. 15.5.

This system of coupling at once gives the gas turbine a very important advantage over the reciprocating engine. With the main shaft separated from the power shaft, the main shaft can be run at full speed when the vehicle is at rest, and the full velocity of the hot gases is then directed on to the power turbine blades. When the power turbine is at rest, the impact of the gases is most powerful—in other words, maximum torque is available at starting and torque falls off as the vehicle accelerates. This is the ideal characteristic for road transport, since it provides maximum acceleration at low speed and enables an increase in hill gradient to be accommodated by a reduction of vehicle speed without the necessity for changing gear. A gear box is not therefore essential in a gas-turbine car, though a simple 2-speed box is required in practice to permit reversing and to enable high speed to be realized without sacrificing acceleration. Gear changing, however, will be much less frequent. The main controls will be the accelerator and brake pedals. When the hand brake is released and the accelerator pedal is depressed (thus increasing the fuel supply to the combustion chamber), the vehicle will move forward and accelerate to perhaps 60 m.p.h. without any other operation. The top speed of, say, 80 m.p.h. will be obtained by moving into the second gear. On release of the accelerator, the vehicle will coast along at a fairly steady speed in contrast to the petrol engine car which slows down as a result of the engine braking effect. A gas-turbine car in this form requires rather more frequent use of the foot brake and hence causes greater heating and wear of the brakes. The absence of the engine braking effect is rather a disadvantage, and designers

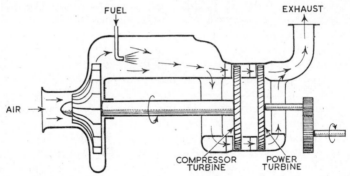

*Fig. 15.5. A simple automobile gas turbine. Separate turbines are used for the compressor and for the power output*

are already seeking ways of making the gas turbine give a braking effect when the accelerator pedal is released.

The advantages of the gas turbine outlined above are overshadowed by a serious disadvantage. A gas turbine in this simple form uses very much more fuel than a petrol engine of the same power—something like 70 per cent more even for a well designed engine. Consequently most of the thought devoted to the development of the gas turbine for automobiles has been directed towards finding a way of reducing its excessive fuel consumption. The only way of achieving this, apart from minor improvements in design and efficiency which only achieve a small part of the result required, is to provide the engine with a heat exchanger. A simple type of tubular heat exchanger is illustrated in Fig. 15.6. The exhaust gases are led through ducting from the power turbine and made to flow over the outside of the tubes before escaping to the atmosphere. Further ducting is introduced between the compressor and the combustion chamber so that the compressed air flows through the tubes and picks up heat from the exhaust gases before entering the combustion chamber. Thus the air enters the combustion chamber at a higher temperature than before and the fuel supply to the combustion

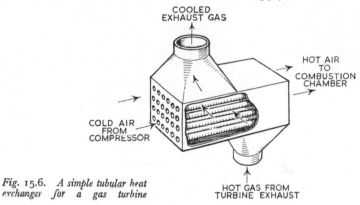

*Fig.* 15.6. *A simple tubular heat exchanger for a gas turbine*

chamber can be reduced without altering the temperature of the air as it leaves the combustion chamber. In this way, the fuel consumption of the gas turbine can be considerably reduced and made comparable with or even better than that of a petrol engine. However, the heat exchanger, and its associated ducting, add considerably to the cost and bulk of the engine and the design of a really attractive heat exchanger installation remains an outstanding problem. At least two types of heat exchanger offering considerable promise are under development. One is the plate type in which the compressed air and hot gas flow sandwich-wise through a stack of flat metal plates. The other is the rotary heat exchanger or regenerator in which the hot and cold streams flow in opposite directions through a porous, rotating disc or drum.

The gas turbine uses several times as much air as a petrol engine of the same power, and disposal of the exhaust gases is therefore more difficult. By lowering the temperature of the exhaust gases, the heat exchanger simplifies the problem to some extent. Rear-mounting of the engine eliminates the need for long and expensive ducting, and it should not prove impossible to dispose of the gases at reasonably low velocity without inconvenience to other traffic. Another difficulty that arises with automobile gas turbines is the time lag in acceleration.

Maximum power is not delivered until the compressor is rotating at 20,000 r.p.m. or more. Unless the inertia of the rotating parts is kept small, the time lag from idling to maximum power may be considerably more than on a petrol engine.

Small gas turbines are less efficient than large ones, owing to the relatively high pressure losses in small turbine blades. It is therefore probable that the first commercially successful application of the gas turbine will be to the larger, more expensive, and more powerful cars, and to heavy commercial vehicles, though in the latter field the gas turbine has to compete with the extremely economical diesel engine.

### The Free Piston Engine

The free piston engine has been successfully used in large sizes for railway locomotives and at least one comparatively small engine has

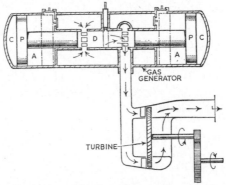

*Fig. 15.7. The free piston engine. A gas generator containing two oscillating pistons P supplies hot gases under pressure to a power turbine*

been designed and tested in a motor car. The engine combines part of a diesel engine with part of a gas turbine to give an engine which has some of the advantages of both. The diesel engine part is used, not for its shaft power, but to provide hot exhaust gases which it delivers under pressure: this part of the engine is therefore called the " gas generator ". The hot gases are supplied to a turbine which functions in the same way as the power turbine of a gas turbine engine. All the engine power is derived from this turbine which is coupled to the output shaft through a speed reduction gear.

The essential features of the free piston engine are illustrated in Fig. 15.7. The gas generator part of the engine has two rather massive pistons P with a single diesel cylinder between the smaller ends of the pistons. When the two pistons slide towards each other, the air in the space D between them is compressed to a high pressure and temperature.

Fuel is injected into the small space left at the end of compression and the fuel burns spontaneously as a result of the high compression temperature, just as in the diesel engine. The pressure rises sharply as a result of combustion and the pistons are forced apart at increasing speed. The outer ends of the pistons are much larger in diameter and slide in two larger cylinders. The energy from the firing is used up in compressing the air trapped in the two cushion spaces C on the outer sides of the two pistons. Whilst the pistons are moving outwards, fresh air is being drawn into the compressor cylinders A from the atmosphere through non-return valves in the cylinder walls. When the pistons reach the end of their outward travel, the ports at both ends of the diesel cylinder are uncovered. Hot gases under pressure rush through the exhaust ports to the gas turbine, whilst fresh air comes in through the inlet ports from the reservoir space surrounding the diesel cylinder. The reservoir space is kept charged with compressed air by delivery from the compressor cylinders through non-return valves during the inward movement of the pistons. The power for the inward movement is provided by the air compressed in the cushion spaces.

The free piston engine has an extremely low fuel consumption, better than the plain diesel engine itself. Although the engine includes reciprocating motion, the two pistons balance each other perfectly, and running should be far smoother than in a crankshaft engine. Furthermore, the use of a turbine ensures a smooth drive and good starting acceleration. However, the need for large compressor pistons makes the engine rather bulky, and there are other design problems such as controlling the piston travel under varying load. Like the gas turbine, the free piston engine is most attractive for large powers and there is little likelihood of its making any early appearance in the field of small or medium-sized cars.

### The Gas Engine

The gas engine functions in the same way as the petrol engine, the only essential difference being that the fuel used is some kind of gas and a gas mixing device takes the place of the carburettor. Most existing gas engines are large, heavily built, single-cylinder engines designed for stationary use, but, with slight modification, the modern automobile petrol engine can be made to run on gas.

Except in parts of the world where petrol is scarce and expensive, or natural gas is particularly cheap, there is no advantage to be gained by a conversion from petrol to gas, whilst a serious disadvantage is introduced, namely, the difficulty of carrying a supply of gas. In the two world wars, many vehicles carried flexible gas bags on the roof, but, even with an enormous bag, the range was less than could be obtained from a gallon of petrol, and the petrol shortage would have to be particularly acute before this scheme could be regarded as at all attractive. Gas can be stored more conveniently and in greater quantity by keeping it under pressure in steel cylinders, but the cylinders must be heavily built to withstand the high pressure and would be very heavy and costly compared with an ordinary petrol tank. Another approach was adopted in the last war, when many vehicles carried portable gas plants mounted on trailers. These plants produced a combustible gas containing hydrogen and carbon monoxide from the partial combustion of a solid fuel such as coke in the presence of water vapour. Clearly the fire cannot be kindled and extinguished instantly and runs of short duration would be quite impracticable. Compared with the convenience of petrol, the system is cumbersome and there is no likelihood of its use in normal times.

### The Electric Car

The idea of the electric car goes back to the early days of the motor car and by 1905 several successful electric vehicles had been constructed. Although the petrol engine has developed far more rapidly, the electric car remains an extremely attractive proposition that awaits a single development—a compact, long-life, reasonably inexpensive storage battery. The car is driven by an electric motor supplied from a storage battery, the drive being taken to the front or rear wheels through suitable gearing. An electric motor can be designed to give high starting acceleration, and the vehicle can be brought up to full speed without change of gear. A clutch is therefore unnecessary, the only controls being an accelerator to control the motor, and a brake. Not only can the motor be used to assist in braking to an even greater extent than is possible with the petrol engine, but it is possible to design the system so that the energy absorbed by the motor is restored to the battery, both when the car is slowing down and when it is descending a hill at steady speed. The electric motor is silent and free from vibration, its maintenance costs are very low, and its oil requirements are so low as to be negligible. These are the internal advantages, but there are other advantages of wider significance.

The electric motor uses no oxygen and discharges no exhaust gases into the atmosphere; if the electric motor should ever replace the petrol and diesel engines in considerable numbers, the air in our cities would be very much cleaner. Furthermore, since most private cars are not required during the night, their batteries could be recharged from the mains at a time when the load on the power stations is small and electricity is cheaper. It would no longer be necessary to have large numbers of road tankers carrying bulk supplies of petrol across the country, since the power used by electric vehicles would be distributed efficiently by the national grid, and would be derived from home-produced coal, low grade oil and atomic energy.

In the early stages of development, the cost of the electric motor and its control gear might well make the electric car more expensive than the petrol engine version, but mass production could be expected to reduce the difference. The main difficulty remains the need for a satisfactory storage battery. Present day designs only have the capacity for such applications as delivery vans and factory trolleys.

### The Steam Car

The steam car was able to compete successfully with the petrol-engined vehicle for several years in the early days of the motor car. The design of steam engines and boilers was well advanced long before the petrol engine existed, and the designer of an automobile steam engine could draw on a large fund of experience. But compared with the petrol engine, the plant required for a steam car was elaborate and bulky as well as being more difficult to control and having a higher fuel consumption; consequently the steam car gradually disappeared.

The chief requirements for a steam car power plant are a steam engine and a boiler. The steam engine comprises a piston and cylinder and a crankshaft mechanism, and is supplied with steam from the boiler. A supply of water must be carried, and a pump is required to feed the water to the boiler. Whilst the exhaust steam from the engine could be discarded to the atmosphere, a very large amount of water would have to be carried to give the car a reasonable range of operation, and this water would be so much extra weight to carry. To avoid this difficulty, steam cars were fitted with a steam condenser, cooled by air in the manner of the modern radiator. A large part of the exhaust steam could thus be condensed into water and returned to the boiler by the feed pump. Whilst coal or coke could be used to fire the boiler, petroleum fuel is more convenient in a steam car, since it makes starting quicker, regulation easier, and keeps the boiler cleaner.

The only advantage of the steam engine is its ability to deliver full torque when the engine is at a standstill, and therefore the clutch and gear box can be dispensed with. To compete in power with the modern petrol engine, steam engines would have to be developed to run at much higher speed than their predecessors. Alternatively, the reciprocating steam engine might be replaced by a steam turbine. But, in either case, the size of condenser required to cope with the large volume of steam would probably be prohibitive. Apart from this difficulty, there remain the disadvantages of high fuel consumption and the fact that, whilst the petrol engine has its own internal combustion, the steam engine requires an external boiler. Even on the railways, the

175

future for the steam engine looks dark; it is certainly no brighter on the roads.

## The Atomic Car

Any engineering plant that makes power available from a rotating shaft is theoretically capable of propelling a motor vehicle. Atomic energy is already being used for turning the shafts of electrical generators and submarines, and the possibility of its application to ships and to aircraft is being investigated. It is therefore natural to consider whether a motor vehicle powered by atomic energy is possible and whether it would have any advantages over the petrol engine.

An atomic engine could be similar in operation to a gas turbine, the only difference being that in the gas turbine the temperature of the air is raised in a combustion chamber by the burning of fuel, whilst in an atomic engine the air would be heated by the energy from a nuclear reactor. The disintegration of uranium atoms in the reactor would provide a source of heat, but the rate at which the uranium was used would be so small that the initial charge of uranium installed in the reactor would last the life of the car—refuelling would never be required! Unfortunately this dazzling prospect is soon shattered by the overwhelming engineering and radiation difficulties in the design of a suitable reactor and heat transfer system from the reactor to the air. A nuclear reactor generates radiation as well as heat, and this radiation can be a source of danger to human health and life. Great care must be taken to ensure that radiation cannot escape from the reactor in dangerous quantities. The reactor would have to be shielded inside a thick concrete container whose size and weight would be so great as to defy installation in any reasonable size of motor car. We are compelled to the conclusion that the atomic car is a dream belonging to the distant future.

Chapter 16

# WHEELS, TYRES AND BRAKES

OF all the inventions incorporated in a modern motor car the wheel is undoubtedly the oldest and any discussion of it may appear superfluous. Yet it is clearly no less important than the engine itself, since a car without an engine can at least be towed. A short discussion of the two main types of wheel, namely the disc and the wire types, is therefore included in the present chapter. Tyres can also be divided into two groups, namely, those which have inner tubes and those which are tubeless; both types are dealt with in the section on tyres.

After some general remarks on the braking problem, the ordinary expanding-shoe drum brake is discussed. Most modern cars use a hydraulic system for transmitting the force applied at the brake pedal to the individual brakes, and this subject is dealt with next. Then there is a discussion of the disc brake, now in use on several high-performance cars. The continual increase in power and speed has led to the development of brakes requiring high operating pressure. The last section deals with the system of using the partial vacuum in the engine induction manifold for increasing the braking pressure applied.

**The Disc Wheel**

Early motor cars naturally used wheels of similar design to those used on horse-drawn carriages, the wheel consisting of a thin rim attached to a central hub by a dozen or so slender spokes. The modern wheel has developed in a series of stages which have progressively eliminated the spokes. Nowadays most wheels consist of two main parts: a steel rim shaped to receive the tyre, and a pressed steel disc in the shape of a dome which takes the place of the spokes (Fig. 16.1). The disc may be riveted or welded to the outer rim and usually has a small number of narrow slots near the rim to encourage the cooling of the brake drums. The wheel is provided with four or five bolt holes and is secured to a flange which is attached to the axle shaft.

It is important for the wheels to be mounted centrally; if, for example, a wheel 22 in. in diameter is mounted $\frac{1}{10}$ in. off centre, then at 60 m.p.h.

there is a tendency for the car to be alternately raised and lowered $\frac{1}{10}$ in. at a rate of 15 times a second, causing troublesome vibration. Central mounting can be ensured either by making the stud holes fit closely round the studs or by arranging for a central hole in the wheel disc to register with a lip on the mounting flange.

The wheel is usually embellished by covering the centre with a chromium plated or stainless steel hub cover. This may be secured to the wheel by springing it over three lugs on the wheel disc; the cover is removed by prising it off with a screwdriver.

**Wire Wheels**

Whereas the disc wheel evolved by the spokes becoming more and more stubby and finally merging into a solid disc, the wire wheel is the

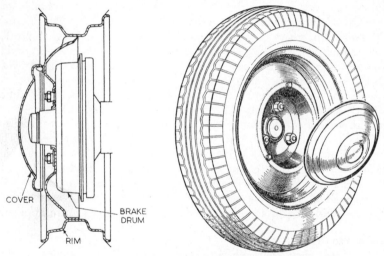

COVER

BRAKE
DRUM

RIM

*Fig. 16.1. A modern pressed-steel disc wheel. The studs securing the wheel to the axle pass through the end face of the brake drum. The cover is mainly an embellishment and is sprung into position over three lugs*

result of an opposite trend. Unlike the disc wheel, the wire wheel has a separate hub which is attached to the rim by a large number of slender wire spokes (Fig. 16.2). The spokes are arranged at different angles and their combined tensions enable the forces due to weight, braking and the drive itself to be transmitted between the hub and the rim. The spoke tensions are adjusted by the screw nipples which secure the spokes at the rim. This construction results in a wheel which combines light weight and high strength with excellent cooling of the brake drums. The wheel is secured by a large wing nut which screws the hub against a conical face. Wheel change is very quick since there is

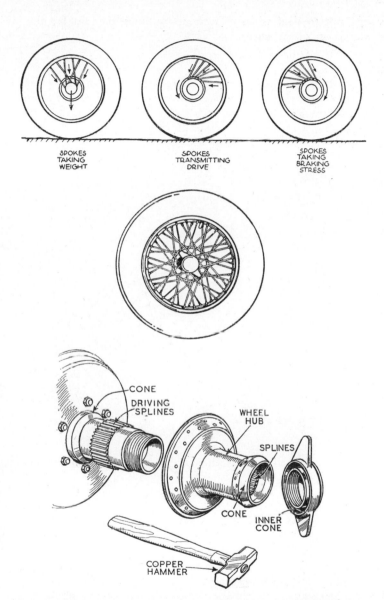

SPOKES
TAKING
WEIGHT

SPOKES
TRANSMITTING
DRIVE

SPOKES
TAKING
BRAKING
STRESS

CONE

DRIVING
SPLINES

WHEEL
HUB

SPLINES

CONE

INNER
CONE

COPPER
HAMMER

Fig. 16.2. *Wire wheel construction. The wheel slides on to a short stub shaft and the drive is taken by splines. The wheel is secured by a large wing nut which can be tightened or loosened by striking the wings with a soft-headed hammer*

only one nut to deal with.   These advantages account for the use of wire wheels on racing and sports cars.

## Tyres

The traditional pneumatic tyre consists of a durable outer cover which takes the weight and wear, and a thin inner tube which acts as a pressure-tight air container.   Recent years, however, have seen the " tubeless " tyre introduced on a wide scale.   A tubeless tyre consists of an outer cover which is made air-tight by means of a special lining

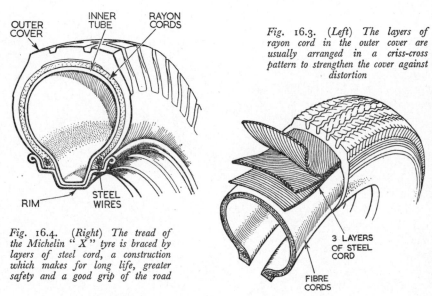

OUTER COVER   INNER TUBE   RAYON CORDS

RIM   STEEL WIRES

*Fig.* 16.3.   *(Left)   The   layers   of rayon   cord   in   the   outer   cover   are usually   arranged   in   a   criss-cross pattern to strengthen the cover against distortion*

3 LAYERS OF STEEL CORD

FIBRE CORDS

*Fig.* 16.4.   *(Right)   The   tread   of the Michelin " X " tyre is braced by layers   of   steel   cord,   a   construction which   makes   for   long   life,   greater safety   and   a   good   grip   of   the   road*

and which seals itself against the rim of the wheel; a separate inner tube is not required.

The general construction of the tyre is similar for both the tubed and tubeless types (Fig. 16.3).   Layers of strong rayon cord are moulded into rubber forming a strong wall upon which the outer tread is built.   The cords of alternate layers run in crossing directions to strengthen the tyre against distortion.   The inner edges of the tyre are built round rings of high-tension steel wire which give the casing a pair of strong shoulders for bearing against the wheel rim.

On the Michelin X tyre, the rayon cords are laid at right angles to the tread instead of in a criss-cross pattern.   Also, the tyre is strengthened by three layers of steel wire embedded between the tread and the rayon cording.   This construction is designed to provide a supple tyre wall in combination with a firm tread which will grip the road well (*see* Fig. 16.4).

Many different patterns are used on the tyre tread, all of them designed to resist slipping. A wheel can move relative to the road in two ways. It can roll along the road as it does during steady cruising and during moderate acceleration, braking and cornering; under these conditions, the part of the tyre in contact with the road is instantaneously at rest. Or the tyre can slide relative to the road as it does when the wheels are locked as a result of violent braking, when the back wheels slip during rapid acceleration, and when the wheels slide sideways during fast cornering. Once the tyres start to slip, control over the car is reduced. Clearly, if the wheels are locked and the tyres are skidding along the road it is impossible to steer the car and equally impossible to slow the car down more quickly by applying the brakes still harder. Similarly, if the back wheels slip during acceleration, then opening the throttle

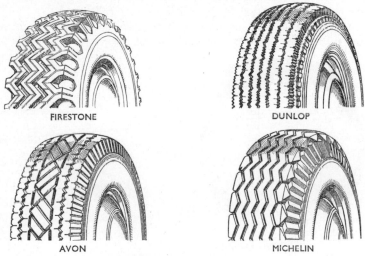

FIRESTONE  DUNLOP

AVON  MICHELIN

*Fig. 16.5. Patterned tyre treads are designed to improve the grip of the tyre on the road. The rougher the road, the rougher is the required tread*

still further will simply cause the wheels to spin faster without increasing the acceleration.

Much experimental work has been carried out in order to develop treads that will combine good skid-resistance with long life and quiet running. Some of the treads used are shown in Fig. 16.5. Often the same tread is supplied on both tubed and tubeless tyres.

One of the functions of the tread is to break up the film of water on a wet road and thus reduce the slipping tendency. On a rough surface most treads are no better than a smooth tyre since the patterned tyre contacts the road in much the same way as a smooth one. But if the road surface is smooth, a patterned tread effectively breaks up the contact area. If, however, the road is extremely smooth and slippery, patterned treads can do little to prevent skidding. A few shovels of fresh grit are required.

The life of a tyre depends very much on how the car is driven, and may vary from 5,000 to 50,000 miles. As the performance and the suspension of the car improve, the driver is encouraged to faster acceleration and cornering, and he tends to use his brakes more. These factors, added to fast cruising, naturally reduce the life of the tyres. Abnormal rates of wear can be avoided by ensuring that the brakes are correctly adjusted, the front wheels properly aligned, and the tyres inflated to the recommended pressures. Switching the tyres of the car round every two or three thousand miles helps to ensure uniform wear. It also provides a convenient opportunity for removing any sharp grit that has become embedded in the rubber.

When first introduced, the tubeless tyre held its air very much better than the tubed tyre because its special lining was more impervious to air

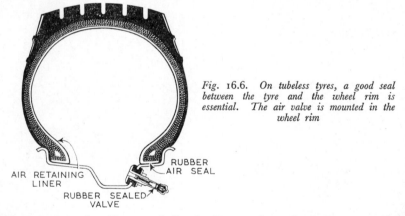

Fig. 16.6. On tubeless tyres, a good seal between the tyre and the wheel rim is essential. The air valve is mounted in the wheel rim

AIR RETAINING LINER

RUBBER SEALED VALVE

RUBBER AIR SEAL

than the natural rubber used for the inner tubes of tubed tyres. Since the introduction of synthetic materials for inner tubes, the difference in behaviour has become less noticeable.

Improvements in both roads and tyres have combined to make punctures fairly rare occurrences. If one does occur, the conventional tubed tyre is at a disadvantage since the inner tube can be repaired only by removing the outer cover. A tubeless tyre, however, can be repaired simply by plugging the hole, provided the hole is not too large. A further advantage is that a tubeless tyre will retain air for a long period even when penetrated by a nail or suchlike, provided the object is left in position. The tubeless type, however, is subject to leakage around the rim in the event of a faulty seal and to sudden deflation if the rim becomes seriously damaged.

Whether the tyre is tubed or tubeless, the air is pumped in through a simple, non-return valve of the Schrader type. The valve seat screws into the valve holder and seals itself by means of a tapered rubber bush. The valve itself has a rubber face and is normally held against the valve seat by the combined pressure of a spring and the air in the tyre. A particle of dirt on the valve face can prevent the valve from sealing properly. To keep the mechanism clean, a valve cap should be fitted to each tyre valve. On modern inner tubes the valve holder is bonded into a short rubber tube and is a permanent part of the inner tube. On tubeless tyres, however, the valve holder is a separate component which is attached to the rim of the wheel as shown in Fig. 16.6.

### The Braking Problem

Any moving body, whether it is a rifle bullet or a motor car, possesses a store of energy by virtue of its velocity. In the case of a motor car, the kinetic energy as it is called has been derived from the engine during the acceleration period. When the car is brought to rest, this energy has to be absorbed in some way. If the car is travelling up a hill, it can be brought to rest by stopping the engine; the energy is then absorbed in carrying the car to a greater height. On a level road, however, the car would go on travelling forward at the same speed for ever, were it not for the effects of wind resistance, bearing friction and suchlike. One way of stopping the car quickly would be to fit a much larger dynamo and to make this charge up a large battery; the kinetic energy would then be absorbed in driving the dynamo. This system is attractive since no energy is wasted; however, the cost and weight of such a system render it unsuitable for motor cars. In practice the energy is absorbed in friction brakes which convert it into heat, and unless adequate air cooling is provided, the brakes may become very hot and hence ineffective. When a medium-sized car is brought to rest from 60 m.p.h. the loss of kinetic energy is sufficient to boil two pints of water. Three-quarters of this energy is given up by the time the car has been slowed down to 30 m.p.h. If the car is being driven fast with frequent application of the brakes, cooling becomes an important factor in design.

The braking effort on a car is often expressed in terms of " $g$ "; $g$ is the acceleration of a freely falling body and is equal to about 22 m.p.h. per second. If the rate of braking is $0.5\,g$, then the car is slowing down at the rate of 11 m.p.h. per second; if it was originally travelling at 44 m.p.h., then it will take 4 seconds to stop.  Gravitational acceleration is produced by a gravitational force which is equal to the weight of the body.  If the braking rate is 0·5 $g$, the braking force exerted by the tyres on the road is 0·5 of the weight of the car;  for a 2,000 lb car, this amounts to 250 lb per tyre.  It is scarcely surprising that rapid braking shortens the life of the tyres.

### Drum Brakes

The majority of motor cars use drum brakes on all four wheels. To-day, hydraulic operation is practically universal but the essential principle of the drum brake can be explained by considering it in its

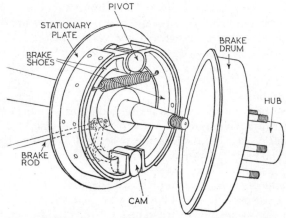

*Fig. 16.7. A mechanically operated drum brake.  When the brake rod is pulled, the cam turns and forces the shoes into contact with the drum.  The same result can be achieved by drawing a wedge between the lower ends of the shoes*

mechanically operated form.  The brake mechanism consists of a pair of rigid, semi-circular " shoes " mounted on a stationary plate and situated inside an iron drum which rotates with the wheel (Fig. 16.7). When the brake is applied by pulling the brake rod and turning the cam, the shoes are " expanded ".  That is, they are forced against the inside wall of the drum by pivoting at their upper ends while their lower ends are forced apart by the cam.  The shoes are faced with an asbestos-base material which produces a high frictional force and at the same time stands up to the high temperature developed without excessive wear. The linings are riveted to the shoes or bonded with a strong adhesive. The riveted type, when worn, can be re-lined by a competent mechanic but the bonded type is a factory job and the complete shoe is usually replaced.

When the linings of a cam-operated brake become worn, the cam has to turn further in order to force the shoes into contact with the drum.

Owing to the changing position of the cam, the force that must be applied to the brake rod to produce a given braking effect varies with the amount of wear. This difficulty is overcome by the Girling wedge-expanded type of brake in which the shoes are forced apart by drawing a wedge between them. Since the wedge angle is constant, the braking effect does not alter as the linings wear.

If the direction of drum rotation is from the operated end of the shoe to the pivoted end, the shoe tends to bite into the drum as soon as a small force is applied to the operated end. A shoe mounted in this way is known as a *leading* shoe. A *trailing* shoe, one whose pivoted end passes a given point on the drum before its operated end, does not share this tendency and does not produce so much braking effect when the same force is applied to its operated end. To get the maximum braking effect, both shoes must be mounted as leading shoes although this necessitates separate operating mechanisms for the two shoes. A popular compromise is to use two leading shoes for the front wheels and one leading and one trailing for the rear wheels. The front wheels can take better advantage of the leading shoes than the rear wheels since the weight on the front wheels increases during braking and there is less likelihood of wheel slip. Also, it is desirable that the front wheels should lock before the rear wheels when the brakes are applied hard in an emergency, otherwise the car is liable to swerve. The trailing shoe on the rear wheels becomes a leading shoe when the car is reversing or when it is parked on a hill facing upwards; thus effective braking is also ensured under these conditions.

Trailing shoes are rather smoother in action than leading shoes and, since they do not depend upon the wedging effect, they are less likely to " fade " with overheating. For these reasons, two trailing shoes are used on the front wheels of high performance cars. Greater braking pressure is required however and power-assisted brakes are necessary.

### Hydraulic Brake Operation

In the past, the brakes were operated by direct mechanical linkages from the foot-brake pedal and the hand-brake lever. Nowadays, the usual arrangement is for the foot brake to operate the front and rear wheels hydraulically while the hand brake operates mechanically on the rear wheels only.

The basic principle of hydraulic operation is illustrated in Fig. 16.8. When the foot pedal is depressed, it forces a piston against the liquid in the " master " cylinder causing the pressure to rise. The brake shoes are operated by " slave " cylinders which are connected to the master by small-bore tubing. When the pressure rises in the master cylinder, the rise is transmitted throughout the system. A force is

7

produced on the piston of each slave cylinder which moves the piston and forces the shoe against the brake drum. As the front wheels have two leading shoes, each shoe requires a separate cylinder. On the rear wheels, however, a single cylinder is used, giving one leading and one trailing shoe. The front-wheel cylinders are rigidly mounted and one end of each cylinder serves as a stationary abutment for the other shoe. The rear-wheel cylinders, however, are free to slide. The hydraulically operated stop light switch can be connected to any convenient point of the system.

It is, of course, extremely important that the whole system should remain full of brake fluid and free from air. The master cylinder illustrated in Fig. 16.9 incorporates a reservoir for this purpose. The spring in the cylinder, in conjunction with the springs attached to the brake shoes, serves to return the master piston when the brake pedal is released. The by-pass port in the cylinder wall causes the system to be replenished from the reservoir and also ensures that the pressure in the system falls rapidly when the brake pedal is released.

On the Lockheed system, the shoes can be opened to compensate for lining wear by inserting a screwdriver through a hole in the wheel disc

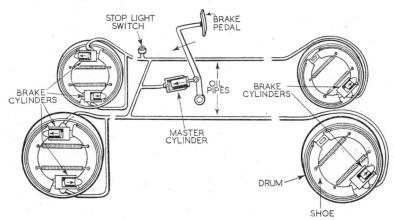

*Fig. 16.8. Hydraulic brake operation. When the brake pedal is depressed, the oil in the master cylinder is compressed and the pressure is transmitted through small pipes to each of the six brake cylinders*

and brake drum and turning an adjuster. The adjuster is, in effect, a cam with a serrated edge and the adjustment is made in steps which can be felt by a series of clicks (Fig. 16.10).

The mechanism for the mechanically operated hand brake, acting on the rear wheels, has to be incorporated in the rear brakes in such a

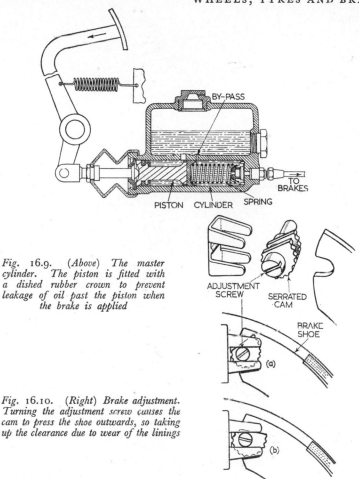

Fig. 16.9. (*Above*) *The master cylinder. The piston is fitted with a dished rubber crown to prevent leakage of oil past the piston when the brake is applied*

Fig. 16.10. (*Right*) *Brake adjustment. Turning the adjustment screw causes the cam to press the shoe outwards, so taking up the clearance due to wear of the linings*

way that the two systems are completely independent. A failure in one must not affect the other. On the Lockheed system a lever, operated by the hand brake, causes the piston to move in the same direction as it does when the foot brake is applied. The Girling rear brake uses a pair of hydraulically operated pistons in a single cylinder with central application of the hydraulic pressure when the foot brake is applied. The action of the hand brake is to draw a wedge piece between the shoe tips, so forcing them apart independently.

The fact that hydraulic brakes have largely superseded mechanical brakes is explained by the simplicity of hydraulic connections and the ease of adjustment. The connecting pipes can be run along in any

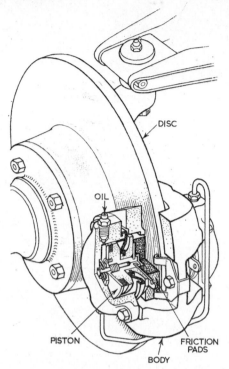

*Fig.* 16.11. *The modern disc brake is reminiscent of the caliper brake used on bicycles. As the heated surface rotates in air, disc brakes are less subject to over-heating than drum brakes*

convenient positions. For most of the length, fixed pipes can be used so that wear and rattle are eliminated. Flexible connections are required only near the wheels themselves. A further advantage is that the same hydraulic pressure is automatically produced at all four wheels; on mechanical brakes the linkage has to be carefully balanced to produce the same effect.

### Disc Brakes

Experience shows that when a car is driven fast its brakes are applied harder and more frequently. Each time the brakes are applied, the temperature of the metal rises and if the brakes are applied frequently, there is insufficient time for the metal to cool. When drum brakes get overheated, they become liable to " fading ": although a high pedal pressure is maintained, the friction force is lower than when the brakes are cool. Also, when the drums become hot they expand, so increasing the pedal travel required to apply the brakes. The trouble can be alleviated by careful design of the drums—for example, the outside of the drums may be covered with cooling fins. The basic weakness of the drum brake, however, is that the frictional surface cannot be directly cooled by the surrounding air; the heat must flow through the drum wall first. With disc brakes, cooling is more direct and brake fading is less of a problem. They are now in use on several high-performance cars and their popularity seems likely to increase.

The motor-car disc brake is basically similar to the caliper type of brake which has long been used on bicycles. The main differences are that the friction pads are applied hydraulically and, instead of being applied to the wheel rim, they are applied to a relatively small disc which rotates with the wheel (Fig. 16.11). The caliper body is stationary and contains two hydraulically operated pistons, one on each side of

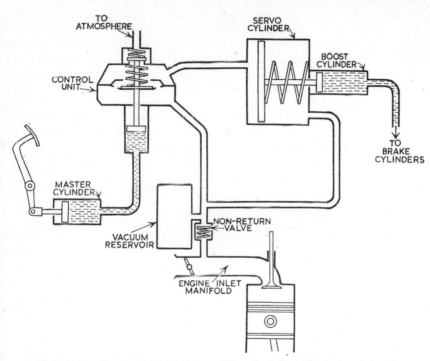

*Fig.* 16.12. *Vacuum-assisted braking. When the brake pedal is free, both sides of the piston in the servo cylinder are exposed to the vacuum and there is no net force. When the brake is applied, the double valve in the control unit moves upwards. Atmospheric air is admitted to the left-hand side of the servo cylinder and the piston in the boost cylinder is forced to the right. Low pressure is maintained in the vacuum reservoir by the connection to the engine inlet manifold, through the non-return valve*

the disc. When the brake pressure is applied, the pistons force the friction pads against the sides of the disc; when the pressure is released, the pads are withdrawn by spring pressure. When disc brakes are used for the rear wheels, mechanical operation by the hand brake must also be provided.

### Vacuum-assisted Brakes

Although disc brakes and trailing-shoe drum brakes are less subject to fading, they require a higher pressure to operate them. To relieve the driver of some of the work, various types of power-assisted brakes have been developed for high-performance cars, most of them making use of the low pressure in the engine induction manifold. The principle of operation is illustrated in Fig. 16.12. The vacuum reservoir is connected to the engine induction pipe through a non-return valve. So long as the engine is running under normal conditions, a continuous partial vacuum is maintained in the reservoir. When the brake pedal is free, both sides of the piston in the servo cylinder are subjected to the vacuum pressure and there is no net effect. When the brake is applied, the valve spindle in the control unit moves upwards and air from the atmosphere enters the left-hand side of the servo cylinder. The force applied to the boost cylinder is considerably greater than that originally applied to the brake pedal. In practice, the master cylinder would also be linked to the boost cylinder so that, in the event of a failure in the servo system, the brakes would still be applied by direct foot pressure.

# Chapter 17

---

# SUSPENSION, SPRINGS AND SHOCK ABSORBERS

UNLIKE the railway train which always has a smooth, steel track before it, the motor car must be able to travel over moderately uneven surfaces without loss of control and without too much buffeting of the occupants. Whether or not it will meet these requirements depends on the design of its suspension, that is, the way in which the wheels are linked to the rest of the car. The suspension is probably the section of motor-car design in which there is more possibility of variety than in any other. It has therefore been necessary to limit discussion to some of the more important types. Springs are discussed as part of the suspension but shock absorbers are dealt with in a separate section.

### The " Horseless Carriage " Suspension

The simplest type of suspension imaginable is one in which the body of the vehicle rests on a pair of beam axles. If road surfaces were perfectly flat and smooth, the arrangement might conceivably be possible; even the best of roads, however, is far from perfect and most cars have occasionally to encounter rough roads containing bumps and pot-holes. Unless some form of springing were incorporated between the wheels and the body, the whole car would be subjected to a continuous shaking which would be very distressing for occupants and vehicle alike. Whilst pneumatic tyres do provide some cushioning, this is insufficient, quite apart from the extreme wear and tear on the tyres if they were called upon to take all the shock.

For 40 years most cars were sprung in the manner of a horse-drawn carriage, laminated leaf springs being interposed between the body and the axle both at front and rear (Fig. 17.1). When a wheel encounters a bump, the axle rises with it but the body is not obliged to rise at the same rate and is therefore relieved of much of the shock. Nevertheless, the axle is still obliged to pivot about the opposite wheel when one wheel meets a bump and this causes twisting of the springs and of the whole structure. In the case of the front wheels, the axle movement is

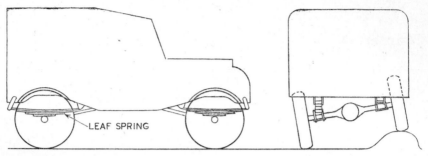

Fig. 17.1. *With this very simple suspension, the body rests on four leaf springs which, in turn, rest on a pair of beam axles*

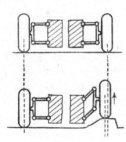

Fig. 17.2. *Parallelogram type of independent front wheel suspension. A true parallelogram causes an undesirable sideways movement of the wheel. This can be avoided by departing from the true parallelogram form*

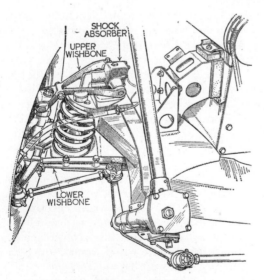

Fig. 17.3. *Modified parallelogram type of I.F.S. The coil spring is compressed between the lower wishbone and a pad on the framework. The shock absorber orms the attachment pivot for the upper wishbone*

particularly objectionable since it can produce unpleasant effects in the steering. Another disadvantage of this type of suspension is that the unsprung weight of the heavy beam axle is inconsistent with good road-holding. When a wheel passes over a bump, it tends to leave the ground for an instant. The spring, which has been compressed in passing over the bump, tends to force the wheel back into contact with the road. Clearly, the lower the weight of the wheel and its associated parts, the more rapidly will contact be re-established and the designer always aims therefore at reducing the unsprung weight. Since the war, there has been an almost complete change-over to independent front-wheel suspension, in order to overcome these difficulties. Most British and American cars, however, retain the twin leaf-spring suspension and beam axle on the rear wheels.

### Independent Front-wheel Suspension

Practically all British cars now use some form of independent front-wheel suspension (I.F.S.). With I.F.S., each front wheel runs on a short stub axle which is linked separately to the chassis or body, so that one wheel can move relative to the body without a corresponding movement of the other. Various types of linkage have been devised, but the parallelogram or wishbone type is by far the most popular (Fig. 17.2). The linkage moves in much the same way as a parallel ruler, but the swinging links are not necessarily of equal length, and the sides of the " parallelogram " may not be parallel. If they were, the wheels would move together or apart as they swung up and down, causing the tyres to scrub sideways on the road surface and increasing the rate of tyre wear. The stub axles on which the wheels revolve are pivoted on swivel pins for steering purposes. These swivel pins serve the same purpose as the " king pins " used with beam axles, the difference being that the two king pins are carried on the beam axle and fixed in relation to each other.

The suspension is, of course, incomplete without a spring to transmit the weight of the car to the wheel. Coil springs are the most popular type, the bottom of the spring being held by the lower " wishbone " while the weight is transferred to the top of the spring from the chassis or body structure (Fig. 17.3). Some suspensions of the parallelogram type use a torsion bar in place of a coil spring. A torsion bar is simply a long rod which is gripped at one end and twisted at the other (Fig. 17.4). The rod may be round or square in section and is, in fact, a spring. On the B.M.C. baby car, the spring consists of a rubber cone compressed between the top wishbone and a retaining housing on the chassis (see Fig. 12.14). On a parallelogram suspension, the wishbones or swinging links must be linked to the wheel in such a way that the wheel can rise and fall and also turn during steering. Thus two distinct motions must be

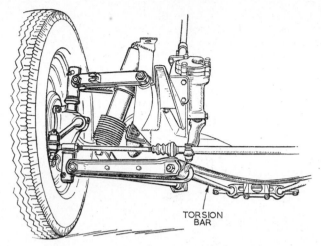

TORSION
BAR

Fig. 17.4. *I.F.S. using a torsion bar and a telescopic shock absorber. The weight of the car is transmitted to the wheel through the lower wishbone. The difference in length of the wishbones reduces side-scrubbing of the tyres*

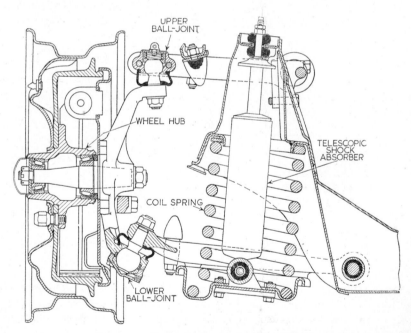

UPPER
BALL-JOINT

WHEEL HUB

TELESCOPIC
SHOCK
ABSORBER

COIL SPRING

LOWER
BALL-JOINT

Fig. 17.5. *Jaguar front suspension using ball joints to permit steering movement as well as rise and fall*

accommodated which normally require two bearings. The suspension can be considerably simplified if ball joints are used since these permit both motions. The Jaguar suspension (Fig. 17.5) uses ball joints at the outer ends of the links so that the " king pins " are completely eliminated and lubrication is considerably simplified. Ball joints are also used on the front suspensions of the Triumph Herald and the B.M.C. baby. Nylon inserts are used on the Triumph to avoid the need for frequent lubrication.

All moving joints in the suspension and steering in which metal rubs on metal must be well lubricated to avoid rapid wear. Usually each joint is supplied with a lubricating nipple which requires a shot of grease or thick oil every thousand miles or so. One way of reducing the number of lubricating points is to use rubber bonded joints in place of metal bearings. This type of joint is often used for linking the wishbone

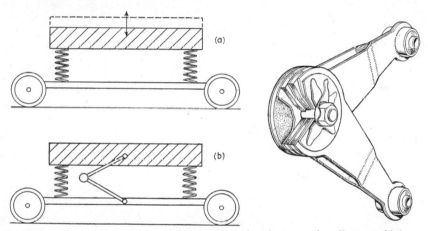

Fig. 17.6. *Oscillations of the weight can be damped out by means of an elbow-type friction damper. This type has been superseded by hydraulic dampers of the piston and telescopic types*

to the chassis. Another advantage of this arrangement is that the amount of road noise transmitted is reduced. Introducing a rubber pad between the chassis and the top of the coil spring has a similar effect.

### Shock Absorbers

The name " shock absorber " is a little misleading since the function of the springs is also to absorb shock. Shock absorbers or dampers are provided to prevent the car from bouncing up and down repeatedly after passing over a bump. If the weight in Fig. 17.6 is forced down on the springs and then suddenly released, it will continue to oscillate up and down until the vibrations are damped out. The time required for the weight to come to rest depends on the amount of " damping " or friction in the system. Rubber has good natural damping properties and if the springs were made of hard rubber the oscillations would soon cease; this is one advantage of using rubber joints in suspension systems. Leaf springs also provide a good deal of internal damping due to the rubbing of one leaf over the other as the spring bends. Steel, however, has very little natural damping and, with coil-spring or torsion-bar suspensions, separate dampers are essential.

One very simple type of shock absorber is shown on the right of Fig. 17.6. Two forked arms are linked together and move like an elbow when the weight moves. The elbow joint contains friction discs clamped together tightly and these introduce the required damping into the system. This type of damper was much used in leaf-spring suspensions, the dampers being attached between the chassis and the axle. Nowadays, however, the hydraulic type of damper is used almost exclusively. This type requires very little attention and can absorb large amounts of energy. It has the added advantage that the damping effect increases with the rate of movement whereas that of the simple friction type is constant. Also the discs of the friction type cannot slip until the load reaches a

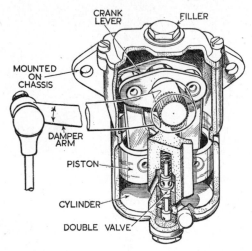

*Fig. 17.7. Piston-and-lever hydraulic shock absorber. Whenever the damper arm moves, oil is pumped from one cylinder to the other. The connecting passage forms a restriction which causes the oil pressure to build up, so resisting the movement of the damper arm. A double spring-loaded valve is provided which opens when the pressure becomes too high; otherwise the damper would become too stiff over a sharp bump*

certain value. Consequently, they introduce undesirable stiffness into the suspension.

On the suspension shown earlier in Fig. 17.3, an Armstrong hydraulic shock absorber forms the support for the upper wishbone. This shock absorber belongs to the piston-and-lever type and its principle of operation can be seen from Fig. 17.7. The shock absorber has two cylinders, each containing a piston which is coupled to one or the other end of a crank lever. The crank lever is attached to a spindle which is turned by the damper arm (often the upper wishbone). The two cylinders are filled with hydraulic oil and when the damper arm turns through an angle, oil is forced from one cylinder to the other through two small holes, one in the end of each cylinder. The rate of oil flow is restricted

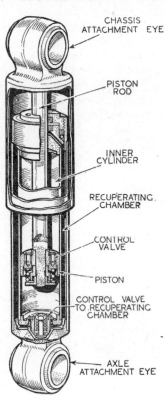

CHASSIS
ATTACHMENT EYE

PISTON
ROD

INNER
CYLINDER

RECUPERATING
CHAMBER

CONTROL
VALVE

PISTON

CONTROL VALVE
TO RECUPERATING
CHAMBER

AXLE
ATTACHMENT EYE

*Fig. 17.8. Telescopic hydraulic shock absorber. On the bump, the piston moves downwards, forcing oil through to the recuperating chamber. On the rebound, the oil above the piston becomes compressed and forces its way through a valve in the piston*

by the small passage sizes, so that pressure builds up in whichever cylinder is compressing. In this way, the movement of the wishbone is resisted and some of the "bounce" energy is absorbed in churning the oil, which therefore becomes hotter. To prevent air from entering the cylinders, the whole mechanism must be kept immersed in oil. The simple action described above is slightly modified by the presence of a double valve in the chamber linking the two cylinders. The valve is really two valves in one and serves as a further restriction on the rate of flow in either direction. If the bump is small, little pressure builds up in the cylinders and then both parts of the valve remain closed; some oil, however, is permitted to pass through small bleed holes in the

197

larger valve. On a more severe bump, the larger valve is forced off its seat and closes on the rebound; similarly the smaller or inner valve opens during the rebound but remains closed during bump movements. By regulating the sizes of the valves, holes and valve springs, the resistances to bump and rebound can be separately controlled and the shock absorber given the desired characteristics.

Another popular hydraulic shock absorber is the telescopic type. Although the construction is very different, the principle of operation is the same as for the type just described. Upward or downward movement of the wheel relative to the body, causes oil to be forced through a restriction, thus transforming the bounce energy into heat. The Newton design, shown in Fig. 17.8, consists basically of a piston and rod fixed to the body or chassis, and an inner cylinder which is attached

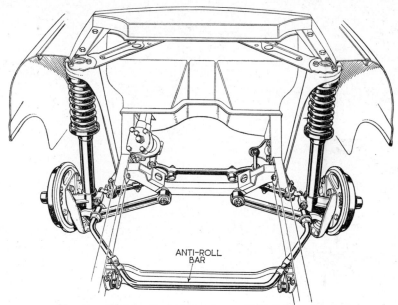

ANTI-ROLL
BAR

*Fig. 17.9  The telescopic shock absorbers on this Ford front suspension serve as part of the linkage in addition to their normal function*

to the wheel suspension and in which the piston slides. A second cylinder surrounds the inner cylinder, forming the recuperating chamber which is simply an oil reservoir. On the bump, when the piston moves downwards in the inner cylinder, oil is forced through a valve in the base of the cylinder into the recuperating chamber. On the rebound, the oil on the upper side of the piston is compressed and forced through a valve in the piston itself. Secondary valves, which are only weakly loaded, are provided in the piston and in the cylinder base to allow the oil to return in the following stroke.

Telescopic shock absorbers can be provided solely for the purpose of damping or they may be incorporated as part of the suspension, as on the Ford front suspension shown in Fig. 17.9. The anti-roll bar linking the two sides helps to equalize the movements and reduce rolling,

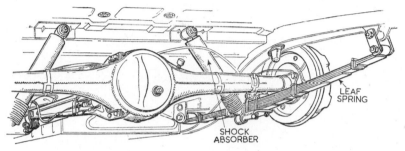

*Fig. 17.10. This conventional rear suspension makes use of a pair of leaf springs and a rigid rear axle. The rear end of the spring is attached to the frame through a short link, to enable the spring to bend freely*

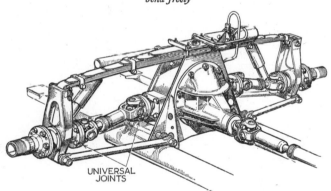

*Fig. 17.11. This independent rear suspension uses a single transverse leaf spring. The differential forms part of the sprung weight. The Triumph Herald employs a transverse leaf spring but makes use of the drive shafts for lateral location of the wheels*

as for example when cornering. Not all telescopic shock absorbers function in quite the same way. On the Armstrong design, the oil flows in a circuit instead of backwards and forwards.

**Rear Suspension**

By far the most common rear suspension is the twin leaf-spring type shown in Fig. 17.10. The great advantage of this design is its simplicity since the springs also serve to locate the back axle and transmit the forward

" push " to the body as already discussed in Chapter 12. The springs
are made by clamping a number of flat steel bars of increasing length
together so that the spring is thickest in the centre where the bending
load is greatest. When the springs flex, there is a certain amount of
sliding movement between the layers and it is therefore desirable for the
springs to be well greased and wrapped with a suitable fabric to retain
the lubricant and exclude dust and grit. Sometimes soft inter-leaves
are placed between the steel layers to reduce friction. The front point
of the spring is located in a rubber bush while the rear end is connected

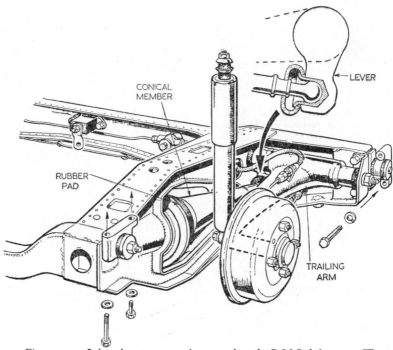

*Fig. 17.12. Independent rear suspension as used on the B.M.C. baby cars. The
wheel is carried on a trailing arm to which is attached a short lever. When the
wheel rises, the lever forces the conical member to the rear, so compressing the
rubber pad*

to the body or chassis through a short link. Without this link, the spring
would be constrained lengthwise and would be unable to bend freely.
Damping is provided by telescopic shock absorbers as shown or by the
piston and lever type.

This Hotchkiss type of drive and suspension, as it is known, suffers
from the disadvantage that none of the weight of the axle and differential
unit is carried by the springs. Independent rear suspension (I.R.S.)

makes it easier to reduce the unsprung weight and makes it possible to achieve better road-holding on uneven surfaces (Fig. 17.11). Until recently, I.R.S. in Britain and America was confined to a few sports cars but it is now being applied on a few popular cars. The B.M.C. baby uses I.R.S. in conjunction with rubber springs (Fig. 17.12). With the rear-engine designs used on several European cars and on the Chevrolet " Compact " car, the close integration of engine, gear box and differential makes it impossible to use a beam type of back axle, and independent rear wheel suspension becomes a necessity.

Two further designs of I.R.S. are shown in Fig. 17.13. The upper one is of the swinging-axle type and has coil springs whilst the lower

*Fig. 17.13. (Right) Two further types of independent rear wheel suspension. In (a), the drive shafts are enclosed and single universal joints are sufficient. In (b), pairs of universal joints are required*

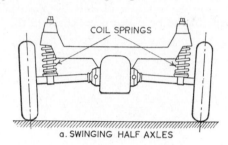

COIL SPRINGS

a. SWINGING HALF AXLES

*Fig. 17.14. (Below) Lancia rear suspension using de Dion axle and twin leaf springs. The differential and brake drums form part of the sprung weight. A Panhard rod provides lateral location between the axle and the frame*

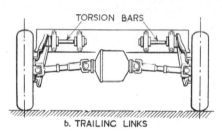

TORSION BARS

b. TRAILING LINKS

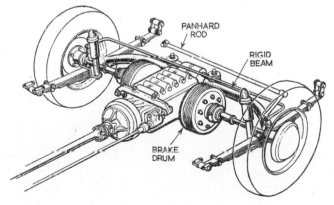

PANHARD ROD

RIGID BEAM

BRAKE DRUM

one uses trailing links combined with torsion bars. In both cases the weight of the differential unit is carried directly by the chassis and is therefore sprung.

The de Dion rear suspension also has a chassis-mounted differential but does not provide independent rear suspension since the rear wheels are carried on a rigid beam which is bowed to clear the differential. The Lancia Flaminia uses a de Dion axle in conjunction with a pair of leaf springs (Fig. 17.14). A bar known as a Panhard rod relieves the springs of the duty of providing sideways location between the axle and the chassis. It will be seen that the brake drums are combined with the differential units. Whilst this arrangement gives a further reduction in unsprung weight and assists brake cooling, it means that the braking torque has to be transmitted through the half shafts and universal joints.

# Chapter 18

# STEERING

STEERING of a car is made possible by the frictional forces that arise between the tyres and the road surface when the front wheels are turned towards the left or right. These forces prevent sideways movement of the tyres so that the wheels always tend to roll in the direction to which they are turned. When these forces are low, as, for example, on an icy road, the wheels are free to move in any direction and steering control is lost.

The present chapter deals with the mechanical linkage used to control the front-wheel movement, and with the gearing used to transmit movement of the steering wheel to that linkage. The use of front-wheel camber and castor is also discussed and the steering behaviour known as under- and over-steer is explained. The chapter concludes with a few words on power steering.

## The Steering Linkage

The simplest way of steering a four-wheeled vehicle is to mount the front wheels on a beam axle pivoted at its centre point, a design often employed by small boys for their street trolleys. The method is unsuitable for motor cars, however, because of the difficulty of arranging for the axle to turn through large angles. It is more convenient to arrange for the front wheels to turn individually about the axle ends although the design of the steering mechanism becomes somewhat more complex.

The essential feature of correct steering is that when the car is following a curved path, each wheel shall be free to travel in a circle about the centre of the curve. This means that, neglecting secondary effects due to tyre slip, each wheel must be at right angles to the centre of the turn; and this centre must lie on a line extending from the rear axle since the rear wheels are not steered (Fig. 18.1(a) ). To satisfy these requirements, the inner front wheel has to be turned through a larger angle than the outer one. If the wheels were turned through equal angles, the car would try to turn about two different centres and the steering

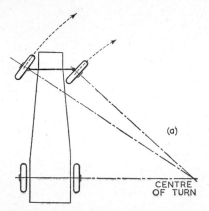

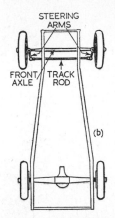

*Fig.* 18.1(*a*). *In order that the wheels shall roll without side-slipping, all four wheels must be perpendicular to the centre of the turn. This means that the inner front wheel must be turned through a larger angle than the outer one*

*Fig.* 18.1(*b*). *The Ackerman steering linkage provides a close approximation to the required front wheel motion. One of the steering arms is operated by the steering wheel*

would be unsatisfactory. Steering systems are usually based on the Ackerman design which gives a fair approximation to the required motion. In its simplest form, each front wheel revolves on a short stub axle extending from a bracket which is pivoted to the front axle and to which is attached a steering arm (Fig. 18.1(b)). The ends of these arms are linked together by a bar known as the track rod. The arms are inclined inwards towards the rear, so that when the track rod moves to the left (i.e. when the car is turning right), the right wheel moves through a larger angle than the left and vice versa. This is the

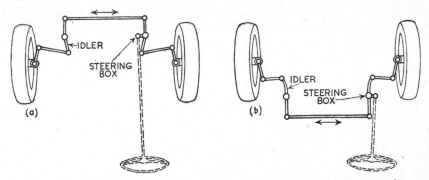

*Fig.* 18.2. *With independent front suspension the simple Ackerman linkage must be modified to permit independent vertical motion of the front wheels. The diagram shows two of the many possible linkages. In both cases the steering box and idler are carried on the frame and each front wheel steering arm is operated through a ball jointed link*

kind of difference required and although the motion does not conform exactly to the ideal, the difference is only serious at or near full lock. The steering arms and track rod can also be located in front of the wheel centres but the principle remains the same. In either case, the movement of the steering wheel is transmitted to one of the steering arms and passed on to the other via the track rod.

With independent front suspension, the front wheels can move vertically relative to one another and the simple Ackerman layout has to be modified to permit this motion without straining the steering linkage. A common arrangement is the use of two levers mounted on the frame of the car, one pair of ends being linked by the track rod while the other ends are linked to the wheels (Fig. 18.2). One lever is embodied in the steering box and is operated by the steering column while the other, known as the idler, is operated via the track rod. The up-and-down motion of the wheels is taken up by the ball joints in the linkage and is not communicated to the track rod. The ball joints are

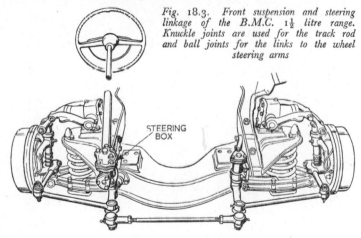

*Fig. 18.3. Front suspension and steering linkage of the B.M.C. 1½ litre range. Knuckle joints are used for the track rod and ball joints for the links to the wheel steering arms*

usually provided with lubrication nipples and protected against dirt by rubber seals which also serve to retain the lubricant.

### The Steering Gear

The smallest circle within which most modern cars can turn is about 35 ft in diameter (this means that the car can turn in a road of this width in a single movement). To achieve this, the front wheels must be capable of turning through an angle of about 30° in either direction. The angle through which the steering wheel must be turned to produce this movement is, however, very much greater and is of the order of one complete turn of the wheel or 360°. Thus there may be a 12 to 1

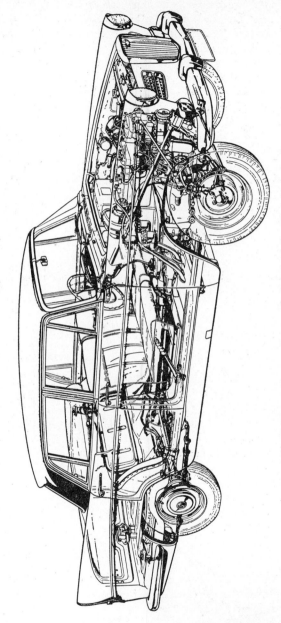

*Fig. 18.4. The Wolseley 15/60 has the same basic body shell and mechanical components as the Austin, Riley, Morris and M.G. saloons of the B.M.C. 1½-litre range. The front suspension and steering linkage is shown in more detail in Fig. 18.3. The steering box is of the type shown on the left in Fig. 18.5*

ratio in the angular movements most of which is accounted for by the steering gear box which transmits the steering-wheel motion to the steering linkage. Without the leverage introduced by the steering gear box, the steering wheel would be hard to turn and very coarse in action.

The steering wheel is usually supported by a fixed tubular column inside which is a rotatable tube linking the steering wheel to the steering box (Fig. 18.3). A general view of the same car is given in Fig. 18.4. The steering box is essentially a gear box in that it has an input shaft (the tube inside the steering column) and an output shaft (operating the steering linkage) and a movement or speed ratio between the two.

One of the steering boxes shown in Fig. 18.5 is of the screw and lever type. A peg in the end of a lever engages with a coarse screw turned by the steering-wheel inner column. The lever is mounted on one end

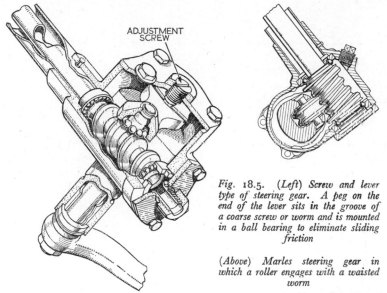

ADJUSTMENT
SCREW

*Fig. 18.5. (Left) Screw and lever type of steering gear. A peg on the end of the lever sits in the groove of a coarse screw or worm and is mounted in a ball bearing to eliminate sliding friction*

*(Above) Marles steering gear in which a roller engages with a waisted worm*

of the steering-box output shaft; on the other end is mounted the " drop " arm which actuates the steering linkage. The Marles cam and roller steering mechanism, also shown in Fig. 18.5, is somewhat similar in action. The peg and lever, however, are replaced by a roller and the screw or cam is waisted to give a profile matching the roller movement. Sliding between the mating surfaces is largely eliminated since the roller is free to turn on its bearings; it follows that friction and wear are correspondingly reduced.

The screw and nut type of steering gear is shown in Fig. 18.6. The screw is made with a coarse thread; that is, the helix is " stretched out "

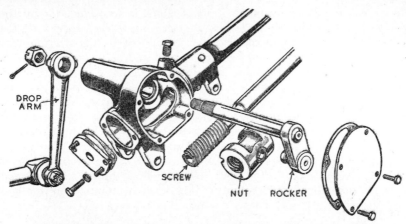

DROP ARM

SCREW

NUT     ROCKER

*Fig.* 18.6. *Screw and nut type of steering gear. The nut is prevented from rotating by a peg which also serves to transmit the motion of the nut to the rocker*

to give a greater movement of the nut for every turn of the screw. This feature ensures that the gear is " reversible "; this means that just as movement of the steering wheel causes movement of the front wheels, so movement of the front wheels causes movement of the steering wheel. At one time it was considered that reversibility was bad since unevenness of the road would transmit movement back to the steering wheel. Irreversibility can be achieved by using a fine screw thread; if a normal screw and nut are held in the hands so that the nut does not rotate, turning the screw will either push or pull the nut, whereas pushing or pulling the nut will not rotate the screw.

Nowadays, reversibility is considered desirable since it can be used to produce such features as automatic straightening of the steering after

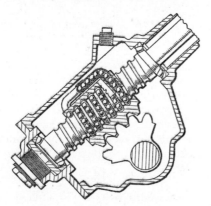

*Fig.* 18.7. *Screw and nut steering gear using re-circulating balls to reduce friction. The nut is free to move along the screw but it cannot rotate*

turning a corner. The screw and nut mechanism can be made reversible by reducing the internal friction or by coarsening the thread. In the recirculating ball type of screw and nut gear shown in Fig. 18.7, friction is reduced to a minimum. As the nut is not free to turn, the motion of the screw feeds the balls to one or other end of the nut; the two ends of the nut are joined by a channel which passes the balls back to the other end. Teeth cut in the side of the nut transmit the movement to a toothed quadrant.

One of the neatest and most efficient steering mechanisms is the rack and pinion type shown in Fig. 18.8. Its action is rather different from that of other types since the rack gives direct side movement which can

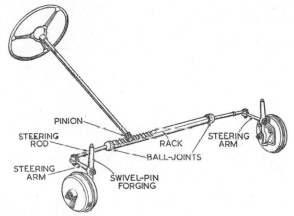

*Fig. 18.8. Rack and pinion steering gear leads to a very simple steering linkage. The rack is carried on the frame and is linked to the steering arms through ball joints to permit rise and fall of the wheels*

be transmitted to the steering linkage without the use of a steering drop arm.

### Centre-point Steering and Camber

If the front wheels were mounted in truly vertical planes and supported on vertical swivels as in Fig. 18.9(a), the steering linkage would be subjected to severe stresses during braking. This is because the force between the tyre and the road in the direction of motion tends to make the wheel and its stub shaft turn on the swivel, thus altering the steering angle of the wheel. Since the wheel steering arms are linked by the track rod, the motion would be resisted, each wheel checking the movement of the other. Nevertheless, it is desirable to reduce the forces in the steering linkage by reducing the turning tendency. The only way to do this is to reduce the effective radius of action of the tyre force since the force itself cannot be eliminated. If either the wheel or the swivel pin or both are inclined at suitable angles to the vertical as in Fig. 18.9(b), the swivel-pin axis intersects the ground at the point of contact with the tyre and there is no turning effort. This arrangement is known as "centre point steering" and the angle of the wheel to the vertical is known as the "camber". True centre point steering is not usually obtained and is not in fact required since it is only necessary to reduce the forces in the linkage to acceptable values. Centre point steering can also be obtained without inclining either the wheel or the swivel pin, simply by locating the swivel-pin axis in the centre plane of the wheel, as in Fig. 18.9(c), but the first arrangement is more usual.

### Front-wheel Castor

A simple castor wheel as used on furniture in the house is a wheel mounted with its axle off-set from a vertical pivot (Fig. 18.10). The

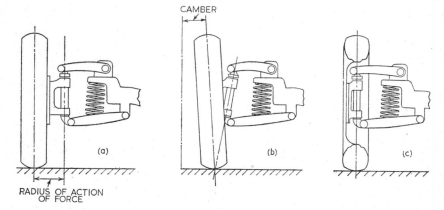

*Fig. 18.9. If the wheel were mounted as in (a), the force between the tyre and the road during braking would tend to alter the steering angle of the wheel and would impose heavy loads on the steering linkage. The arrangements shown in (b) and (c) reduce the radius of action of the force to zero*

article can be steered as it is pushed by giving it a turning force but as soon as it is pushed straight ahead, the castor wheel swings into the straight trailing position. This movement of the wheel is produced by the frictional force between the wheel and the ground which acts towards the rear. The castoring principle is also used on motor-car front wheels so that the wheels tend to straighten out automatically after a sharp turn when the grip on the steering wheel is relaxed. Castoring also helps to keep the car on a straight course in normal

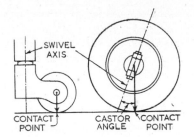

Fig. 18.10. *Furniture castors (left) operate by off-setting the wheel from the swivel axis so that the wheel contacts the ground behind the axis. With the front wheel of a motor car (right) the same result is achieved by inclining the swivel axis*

running so diminishing the effort required from the driver. Castor action on car wheels is achieved by inclining the wheel swivel axis so that it meets the ground in advance of the point of tyre contact. The castor angle is the angle between the swivel axis and the vertical.

### Effect of Side Forces on Steering

If a strong gust of wind hits a car on one side when it is travelling straight ahead, the driver often finds it necessary to alter the steering wheel in order to keep a straight course. The explanation lies in the flexibility of the tyre walls which causes the wheel to creep sideways when a side force is applied (Fig. 18.11). The tyre in the diagram is to be imagined as rolling towards the reader. Creep or slip occurs on all four wheels when a side force is present. The size of the slip angle

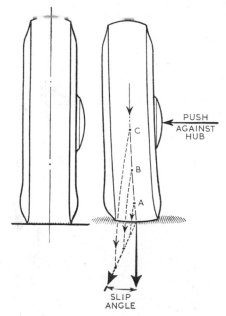

Fig. 18.11. *The effect of a side force is to cause the points A, B and C to meet the ground at the points indicated so that the wheel travels in the direction of the dotted arrow instead of straight ahead*

depends on the flexibility of the tyre, the amount of side force, and the weight carried by the wheel as well as on several other factors. If the slip is greater on the front than on the rear wheels, the car tends to turn away from the wind and must therefore be steered towards it if a straight course is to be held. If the rear-wheel slip is greater, the opposite applies.

### Under- and Over-steer

Strong side forces, and hence wheel slip, also occur during cornering as a result of centrifugal force which tends to move the car sideways,

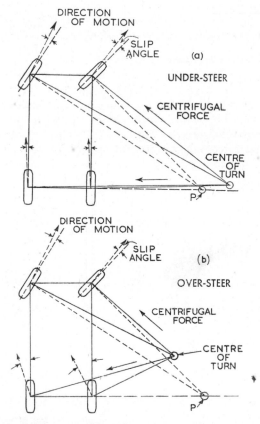

*Fig. 18.12.   Owing to centrifugal force, all four wheels undergo a certain amount of side-slip during cornering.   The true centre of the turn is the meeting-point of the perpendiculars to the actual directions of motion.   The point P shows the centre of turn for zero wheel slip.   When the slip of the front wheels is greater as in (a), under-steer is produced, i.e. the radius of the turn is increased.   Over-steer, the opposite condition, is shown in (b)*

away from the centre of the turn (Fig. 18.12). The effect of slip is to give a radius and centre of turn different from those given by finding the intersection of lines drawn at right angles to the wheels according to the Ackerman principle described earlier. Instead, the lines must be drawn at right angles to the actual directions of motion taking slip into account (Fig. 18.12). If the slip is greater on the front than on the rear wheels, the car tends to turn less sharply than it should for a given

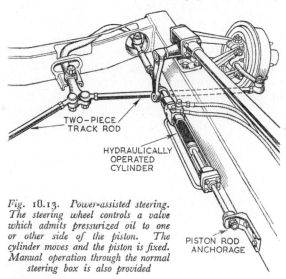

TWO-PIECE
TRACK ROD

HYDRAULICALLY
OPERATED
CYLINDER

PISTON ROD
ANCHORAGE

*Fig. 18.13. Power-assisted steering. The steering wheel controls a valve which admits pressurized oil to one or other side of the piston. The cylinder moves and the piston is fixed. Manual operation through the normal steering box is also provided*

movement of the steering wheel. This condition makes for stability and safety and is known as " under-steer ". If, on the other hand, the rear-wheel slip is greater, then when the car is put into a turn, the effect of centrifugal force is to make the turn sharper. This condition is known as " over-steer " and whilst it makes the car respond quickly to slight movement of the steering wheel and is useful on winding roads, it is not conducive to effortless driving since greater care is required.

The flexibility of the tyres is related to the inflation pressures and adjustment of these gives some control over the steering behaviour. Raising the pressure of the rear tyres, for instance, increases their stiffness and reduces their slip, so tending to reduce over-steer.

### Power Steering

The process of development which resulted in power-assisted brakes, power-operated clutches and automatic transmissions was bound eventually to lead to the introduction of power-assisted steering (it is unlikely, however, that even the most imaginative of designers will

213

attempt to design an *automatic* mechanism capable of steering the car in traffic). Power steering was first developed for commercial vehicles where the effort required to turn the steering wheel, particularly when manoeuvring, can be considerable. Even with private cars, and particularly when low-pressure tyres are used and the weight on the front wheels is high, power steering can result in an appreciable lessening of effort when turning sharp corners or manoeuvring in confined spaces, and it is now in use on several of the larger cars.

The steering is, of course, still controlled by movement of the steering wheel but the wheel turns more easily. Several systems of power steering have been developed, most of them using hydraulic oil supplied at high pressure by a special engine-driven pump. The oil is supplied to one or other side of a piston which is attached to the steering linkage and is free to slide in a cylinder attached to the frame of the car. Alternatively the piston may be fixed and the cylinder free to slide (Fig. 18.13). The oil is admitted to the cylinder through a valve which is operated by movement of the steering wheel. The normal steering gear is retained so that manual steering remains available in the event of a fault in the power system. Furthermore, the system can be designed so that no power is supplied when the steering movement is small in which case a certain amount of manual effort is always required. In this way, the sensitivity and " feel " of the steering are retained.

# Chapter 19

# THE BODY STRUCTURE

WHEREAS changes in mechanical design are comparatively rare and concealed from casual observation, changes in body design are at once both frequent and noticeable. Often the change is simply a minor styling modification and consists of altering a panel here and there and redistributing the chromium plating. Along with these trivial changes, there occurs a genuine process of evolution governed partly by the economics of production and partly by the efforts of designers and engineers to overcome the deficiencies of previous models. The present chapter discusses the design and structure of the modern chassisless body structure and its development from the separate-chassis type of construction. Other aspects of the subject such as streamlining and the materials used in construction are also included.

## The General Trend

If we compare the general structure of a modern saloon car with its pre-war equivalent, we notice many outstanding differences in design and also a few basic similarities (Fig. 19.1). The body space of a car has to be allocated to three main claimants, namely, the driver and passengers, the luggage and the engine. Although a few modern cars have their engines at the rear, the majority continue to employ the pre-war front-engine layout. Another obvious similarity is the continued popularity of four swing-open doors, though nowadays nearly all doors are hinged at the front edges. This is safer than the rear hingeing used on many pre-war cars since wind pressure cannot swing the door open if it is accidentally unfastened.

One of the most outstanding differences to be noted is the blending of the bonnet and wings into a single form which encloses the engine and front wheels and houses the head lamps. The exposed radiator is now a thing of the past and the only outward sign of the radiator's existence is the air intake at the front of the car. These changes in frontal appearance have been associated with the introduction of independent front-wheel suspension. The elimination of the front axle

215

beam made it possible to bring the engine further forward and yet keep it low. At the same time, the new independent suspension had to be accommodated on either side of the engine and required greater height than the leaf-spring suspension. It was therefore natural that the bonnet and wings should merge together.

Forward mounting of the engine has reduced the proportion of total space allocated to the engine and made it possible to seat the passengers centrally within the wheel-base, thus producing a more comfortable ride, and also to increase the size of the boot (Fig. 19.2). Even the

*Fig. 19.1. The modern saloon provides excellent all-round vision for the driver by making extensive use of glass and slender roof pillars. Like its pre-war equivalent it has a front-mounted engine, four doors and drive through the rear wheels; but merging of the bonnet and front wings, elimination of the running boards and enlargement of the boot have completely transformed its appearance*

*Fig. 19.2. On a modern saloon, the engine and passengers are located further forward than on a pre-war car. The rear passengers have a more comfortable ride and there is more room for the luggage boot*

smallest cars nowadays offer very substantial luggage accommodation. The effectiveness of the space is sometimes increased by mounting the spare wheel vertically at one side of the luggage compartment; alternatively it may be housed in a separate compartment beneath the boot.

Another notable development is the increased use of glass above the waistline. The introduction of the curved front windscreen led to a considerable improvement in forward visibility and has been followed by the " wrap-around " or " panoramic " windscreen. With the latter arrangement, the front roof pillars are displaced rearwards, so widening the forward field of view with some sacrifice of sideways vision. At the rear, too, sheet metal has been steadily yielding to glass and, while some may be perturbed by the coming-or-going appearance of many popular saloon cars and others may be embarrassed by the feeling of sitting in a glass-house, everyone welcomes the improved all-round visibility.

The post-war urge of body stylists to outstrip one another in the creation of chromium-plated, dragon-faced juggernauts mercifully appears to

8

have subsided. Several popular cars of recent years bear witness to the fact that it is possible for the modern car to combine good performance and reliability with a graceful and pleasing appearance.

### Farewell to the Chassis?

Ten years ago or so most British cars were built in two main sections—the chassis and the body. A chassis consists of a steel frame, attached to the axles by means of laminated leaf springs or other suspension arrangements and carrying the engine and all other mechanical components. It is a self-contained propulsion system and can in fact be driven on the road by itself. The body section can be built in another

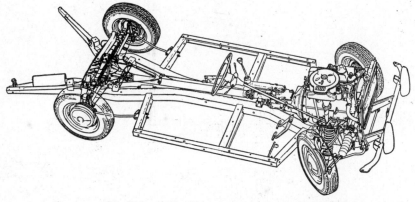

*Fig. 19.3. The Triumph Herald has a separate chassis and independent rear-wheel suspension. It can turn a full circle in a road only 25 ft wide*

part of the factory and lowered on to the chassis and bolted in position shortly before the car is completed. Most American cars are built in this way, but on many popular British and European cars the chassis has disappeared as a separate section and has been integrated with the body. A notable exception is the Triumph Herald, whose separate chassis is illustrated in Fig. 19.3. The Ford Anglia, illustrated in Fig. 19.4, is a car of about the same size and of chassisless construction.

To many motorists, the chassis was the all-important part of the car and its elimination has been accepted with head-shaking as another sign of the times. Yet there are sound engineering reasons for the integration of the body and chassis. The modern car body is built up by welding several steel sections together (Fig. 19.5). These sections are formed in high-power presses by stamping flat sheet steel into shape between a pair of heavy steel blocks or dies having the requisite contours. A sheet of steel, used in the sound-effects room, can be made to rattle like thunder, yet when it is formed into a well-designed pressing, it assumes a strength

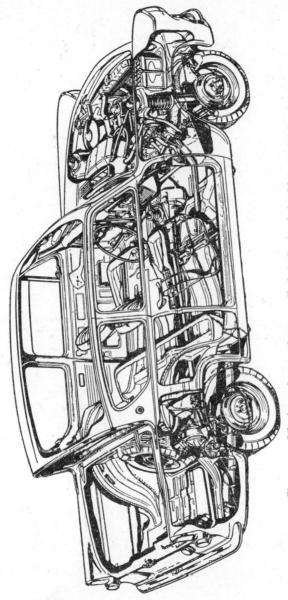

*Fig. 194. Like its predecessor, the present Ford Anglia is of chassisless construction, but an overhead valve engine is now used and the gear box has four speeds instead of three*

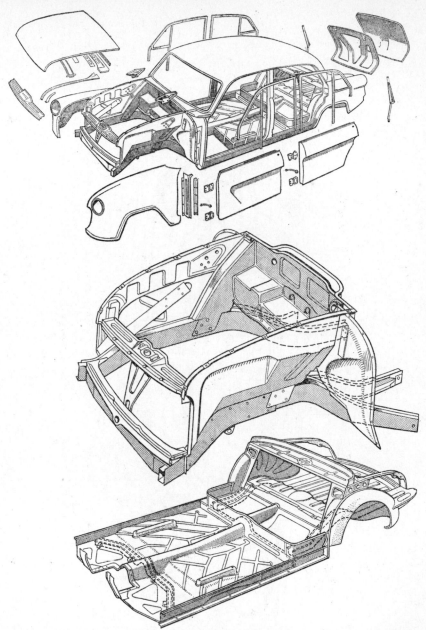

Fig. 19.5. *Most popular British cars are built without a separate chassis. The body is built up from pressed-steel sections, welded and bolted together, and re-inforced to take the weight of the engine and the suspension forces. The illustration shows sections of the Standard Vanguard body*

and stiffness that is very high for its weight. The thickness of steel used for motor-car bodies is small, less than a twentieth of an inch in most places; it is therefore necessary to stiffen many of the panels by welding lengths of steel channel or other sections to them in suitable places. When the roof and floor and other pressings are welded together, the body as a whole is extremely strong and is quite capable of accepting the engine and suspension mounting brackets and resisting the corresponding engine and road forces without any need for a separate chassis frame. Properly designed, a chassisless body has a lower weight than the equivalent body-plus-chassis design, since weight is saved by only reinforcing the structure where the additional strength is required. But as a cynic might well remark, it is hardly to be expected that this form of construction would be adopted by the leading manufacturers unless it led to substantial reductions in cost. As the construction makes efficient use of the raw material, a saving in material cost is to be expected. Moreover, the use of specially designed welding machines which can weld simultaneously at a large number of points leads to cheap and rapid production.

The cost of designing a chassisless car and preparing the tools and fixtures for its production is very high and can only be offset by large scale production. Furthermore, this form of construction does not lend itself readily to continuous development and the separate chassis continues to be used on higher-class and sports cars which are produced in smaller numbers. American preference for the separate chassis may be partly explained by the greater ease with which frequent styling changes can be carried out.

The most vulnerable parts of the car in a minor accident are the wings enclosing the wheels. If the wings are bolted to the main body structure they can be replaced if necessary. If they are welded, however, repair is much more difficult, though it is surprising how readily a skilful panel-beater can restore the shape of a severely crumpled wing. In the event of a serious accident, chassisless construction is likely to lead to more costly repairs than would arise with a car whose body and chassis could be separately rectified. Much of the increased cost of body repairs is attributable to the complex curves used in modern styling and this factor is not peculiar to chassisless construction.

Several popular cars are manufactured in " convertible " as well as in the normal saloon form. The accommodation is similar to that of the saloon but the convertible has two doors instead of four and the front seats tilt forward to allow the rear passengers to enter. With a convertible of chassisless construction, the elimination of the steel roof makes it necessary to reinforce the lower part of the body in order to keep sufficient strength and rigidity. The degree of reinforcement required naturally depends on the extent to which the roof of the saloon contributes to the strength of the body.

### Streamlining and Wind Resistance

Whether or not the trend towards the streamlining of motor cars originated in the various sales departments, there is no doubt that the modern car has a lower wind resistance than a car of similar size thirty years ago. Without this reduction, the high top speeds,

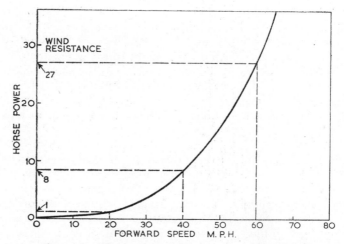

*Fig. 19.6. The power required to overcome wind resistance increases rapidly at high speed (as the cube of the speed)*

and good fuel economy at the fast cruising speeds common to-day, would not be possible, since wind resistance increases rapidly with speed. The horse-power required to overcome this resistance increases as the cube of the forward speed. Thus if the power required at 20 m.p.h. is 1 h.p., then at 40 m.p.h., $\frac{40}{20} \times \frac{40}{20} \times \frac{40}{20} \times 1$ h.p. will be required, that is 8 h.p. At 60 m.p.h., $\frac{60}{20} \times \frac{60}{20} \times \frac{60}{20} \times 1$ or 27 h.p. will be required and so on (*see* Fig. 19.6). Whilst low wind resistance is unnecessary in a car used mainly in urban areas or on poor roads, it assumes major importance if the car is required for fast cruising on motorways.

The perfectly streamlined car would be shaped like a horizontal tear-drop with the bluff end at the front. Nothing quite like this has yet appeared on our roads though certain small " bubble " cars show some tendency towards this form. The tear-drop shape presents serious

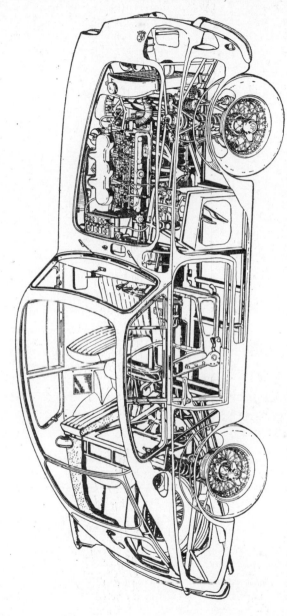

Fig. 19.7. *The A.C. Greyhound saloon (2-litre) has its body built round a tubular "space" structure. Aluminium and glass fibre panels are extensively used in order to save weight. Independent suspension based on coil springs is used both at the front and rear*

design problems and, in any case, it is doubtful whether these lines would meet with a popular reception. Wind tunnel tests show that a tapered rear is more important than correct frontal design, although concealment of the radiator and flush-mounting of the head lamps has certainly produced some improvement. The A.C. saloon with its rear window sloping down to the luggage boot (Fig. 19.7) comes fairly close to the ideal. On the Ford Anglia, however, styling and other considerations appear to have taken precedence over streamlining. The low roof-line of modern cars helps to reduce wind resistance besides improving the general road-holding.

The tail fins used on several modern cars probably owe their existence to their considerable supposed sales appeal but, at very high speed, they can, if large enough, serve a useful purpose in adding to the stability of the car, acting as " straight-ahead rudders".

### Body Materials

*Wood* has practically disappeared as a structural material in body construction, having been displaced by steel in sheet and other forms.

*Steel* can be quickly and easily pressed to shape by mechanical means. It is strong in relation to its weight and it can be joined easily by welding. Another advantage is that it is cheap. Most of the steel used to-day is " mild steel " which is a refined form of iron containing carbon in very small quantities. Ordinary cast iron contains considerably more carbon and tends to be brittle whereas mild steel is not only strong but will bend without breaking. The most serious drawback of mild steel, however, is its poor resistance to the corrosive attack of the atmosphere so that it is seldom possible to use it without some sort of protective coating (*see* Chapter 20).

*Aluminium* has most of the advantages of mild steel together with two of its own: it is light in weight and it has good corrosion resistance even when unprotected. An all-aluminium structure, however, would be costly and would not necessarily be lighter than a steel structure of equal strength. The material is rather prone to cracking and is mainly suitable for parts which carry no loads such as the bonnet top, wings, window surrounds and perhaps bumpers.

*Stainless steel* contains quantities of nickel and chromium and is completely resistant to normal atmospheric corrosion. It is, however, very much more expensive than mild steel and rather more difficult to form into shape. Nevertheless it is being increasingly used for bumpers, grilles and window surrounds since it does not require chromium plating and is more durable.

*Plastics* are still not extensively used on motor car bodywork although they offer considerable advantages. The part can be given its colour during manufacture and never needs painting. A plastic component such as a wing is springy and will take a slight bump without any appreciable damage. Plastic materials, containing glass fibre for greater strength, have been used as the main material for the bodywork of several cars outside the mass production field and it will not be surprising if their use grows. The manufacturing technique, however, is very different from that used with steel and, in view of the vast capital represented by existing machinery, changes are not likely to come rapidly.

# Chapter 20

# BODY DETAILS

A NTI-CORROSION treatment and painting of the welded body shell are the first subjects discussed in the present chapter. The next section deals with chromium plating and is followed by a discussion of the motor-car glass-work, including some notes on " safety " glass and curved windscreens. Matters relating to doors and roofs are then dealt with and the chapter finishes with a section on seating and interior arrangements.

### Paint and Protection

The mechanical parts of a car can be replaced without much difficulty should they become damaged or badly worn and, whilst this is equally true of minor body components such as wings and doors, extensive replacement of the bodywork is unlikely to be economically attractive. The life of the car is therefore largely determined by the life of the bodywork and this in turn depends on the quality of the surface treatment that the body has received at the factory. Paintwork serves not only to give the car a pleasing appearance but also to protect the external surfaces from corrosion. In a country like Britain where damp weather and atmospheric pollution are common, anti-corrosion treatment is particularly important. On hidden surfaces such as floor panels and door interiors, paintwork as such is unnecessary and a less expensive protective coating can be used. In hot, non-industrial parts of the world, corrosion is of secondary importance since the car dries quickly after heavy rain and surface deposits are dusty rather than dirty. In such conditions, the thing that matters is how well the paintwork retains its appearance under the bleaching attack of strong sunlight.

In practice, the general treatment of the bodywork in a modern factory is independent of the final destination of the car. When the bare steel body arrives at the paint shop, it is thoroughly cleaned to remove all traces of grease and an anti-corrosion chemical coating is applied to all surfaces either by spraying or by immersion of the whole body in a tank. A coat of primer paint is then applied and imperfections in the

226

surface are smoothed out by hand-application of "stopping" putty. Further coats of primer and undercoating paint are applied to the outer surfaces to form a base for the final coats of finishing enamel. Although cellulose paint is still used in repair and respray work, it has been largely superseded as the original factory coating by stove-dried enamel. The modern paint shop is highly organized and the drying process between successive coats is reduced to half an hour or so by passing the body through banks of radiant heaters. In some plants, the body is given an electric charge as it passes through the spraying booth in order to attract the paint droplets to the surface.

Present-day colour schemes are very much brighter than before the war and two-colour finishes are fairly common. Before the second colour is applied, the adjacent surfaces are masked with adhesive paper in order to keep the colours separate. Usually the two colours are arranged to meet at a chromium decoration strip or at the beading of a panel joint, thus eliminating the danger of a wavy line between the colours.

Floor panels, wings and other surfaces are often coated on the underside with an adhesive compound in order to reduce body drumming noise and the damage and noise caused by grit and dirt flung up from the road. The factory treatment is only partial, but the facilities for underbody "sealing" with one of the proprietary compounds such as "Underseal" are widespread. Whether or not under-coating is worthwhile depends on the general standard of maintenance which the owner intends to give to the car.

### Chromium Plating

Good quality chromium plating, tastefully used, can enhance the appearance of a car considerably. On the other hand, a good coat of paint is preferable to poor quality plating which soon corrodes and becomes unsightly.

Chromium plating is applied by immersing the part in a solution of chromic acid and passing an electric current through the surface to be plated. The chromium deposited comes from the solution, which must therefore be replenished from time to time. Provided the current is sufficiently high and other conditions are correct, the plating is hard and shiny and requires no special polishing.

The durability of the plating depends on the previous surface preparation. The chromium film itself is extremely thin, being no more than a few hundred thousandth parts of an inch in thickness. Although it appears smooth, it is in fact porous and whilst the chromium itself is resistant to the corrosive attack of a damp atmosphere, it is unable to protect the steel completely. Before the chromium is applied,

227

the part must be given a protective coating of nickel which may be twenty times as thick as the final chromium layer. The nickel seals the steel surface from the atmosphere and the chromium provides the polish, as nickel alone would soon tarnish. The cost of the nickel coating is sometimes reduced by replacing part of it by a layer of copper.

Chromium plating is extensively applied to such parts as bumpers, radiator grilles, wheel hub cover plates, door and window surrounds, door handles and innumerable styling embellishments. The underlying material is usually steel, but chromium plating is also used on brass and other materials. Door handles, for example, are often made of zinc alloy. It appears from current trends, however, that chromium plating must compete increasingly with polished aluminium and stainless steel.

### Glass and Windows

The glass used for the windows and windscreens of motor vehicles has to be of a type that does not form sharp edges when broken. There are two types of " safety " glass in common use, namely toughened glass and laminated glass.

Toughened glass is produced by first heating the glass and then chilling it rapidly in a current of cold air. The principle of the method depends on the well-known fact that most materials, including glass, expand when heated and contract when cooled. The surface layers of the glass cool and contract first and the movement is not resisted by the hot interior which is in a plastic state. When the interior cools, however, its motion is resisted by the cold surface layers which therefore become compressed. The process strengthens the glass in two ways. Glass normally breaks when a blow causes part of the surface to be " stretched " beyond breaking point, and if the surface is initially compressed, breakage is less likely to occur. Moreover, when breakage does occur, the compressed surfaces tend to hold the windscreen together.

Unfortunately, when toughened glass does break, as for example when a stone from the wheel of a passing car strikes the windscreen, the whole area becomes practically opaque (Fig. 20.1). By bringing his face near the glass, the driver may be able to see sufficiently to bring the car to a safe halt; alternatively he should be able to strike a hole with his fist without cutting himself. But the experience can only be very disconcerting.

When *laminated* glass is damaged by a blow, the damage is confined to a much smaller area around the point of contact. Laminated glass such as " Triplex " is made by forming a " sandwich ", which consists of two layers of glass with a thin layer of transparent plastic material between them. The sandwich is bonded together by application of heat

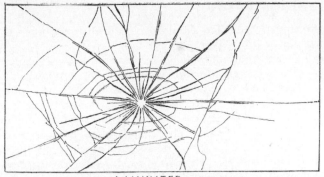

LAMINATED

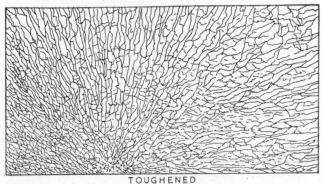

TOUGHENED

Fig. 20.1. *When breakage occurs, laminated safety-glass gives better visibility than the toughened type, but it is more likely to cause injury if part of the body is thrown against it*

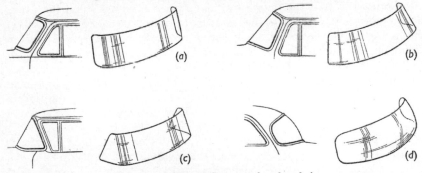

(a)

(b)

(c)

(d)

Fig. 20.2. *Curved glass can be shaped in several ways. This illustration shows the use of*
 (a) *cylindrical curvature*
 (b) *conical curvature*
 (c) *raked pillars*
 (d) *spherical curvature on a rear window*

and pressure and if breakage should occur, the broken glass is held in place by the plastic inter-layer.

In recent years, considerable development has occurred in the application of curved glass to windscreens and rear windows. A curved windscreen, combined with slender and well-positioned pillars, can produce a marked improvement in forward visibility. The first screen in Fig. 20.2 is blended from cylindrical surfaces whilst the second is formed from conical surfaces. The raked pillar used with the third windscreen shown, improves forward visibility at low level but does not appear to improve visibility at eye-level. Moreover the corners present serious blind-spots in wet weather, since the wiper action has to be confined to the centre regions where curvature is low. The rear window shown in the same illustration introduces spherical curvature and provides good rear vision.

Side windows are usually operated by a winding handle though certain luxury cars are equipped with electric push-button control. A typical winding mechanism is shown in Fig. 20.3. A friction device in the mechanism prevents the window from moving except when the handle is turned. Hinged " quarter " windows or louvres are now widespread as a means of providing ventilation without unpleasant draughts.

### Doors and Roofs

The doors of the modern car are of welded, sheet-metal construction. They are usually of substantial thickness but are, of course, hollow and contain the door lock and window winding mechanism. Nowadays, the doors are hinged at the forward edges and often a friction device is incorporated so that the door can remain open unaided when the car is sloping sideways. Access to the inside of the door is obtained by removing the inside panel. Cars in the lower price range make frequent use of spring clips for securing panels and fittings to the bodywork (Fig. 20.4). Although the method is economical, it is not very attractive engineering and rather encourages rattles. Another method for the attachment of fittings is the self-cutting panel screw. If the screw is turned too tightly or undone too many times, one is left with an enlarged hole in the panel and a loose screw.

The introduction of the push-button type of external door handle is welcome since it is more robust than the pivoted type and one can take a firmer grip (Fig. 20.5). Passengers' doors are usually locked either by a reverse movement of the inside handle or by movement of a separate catch. Some models are fitted with additional concealed locks for greater safety with children. The driver's door is usually locked by a key from the outside, so that it is impossible accidentally to lock oneself

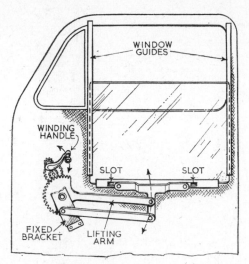

Fig. 20.3. *Window winding mechanism. The winding handle is geared to a toothed quadrant on one end of the lifting arm*

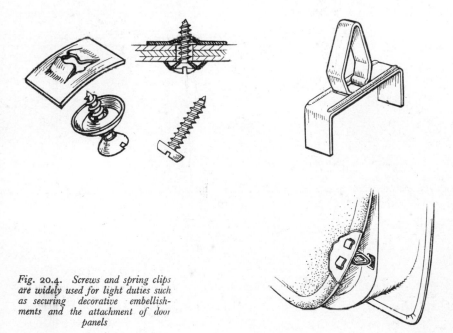

Fig. 20.4. *Screws and spring clips are widely used for light duties such as securing decorative embellishments and the attachment of door panels*

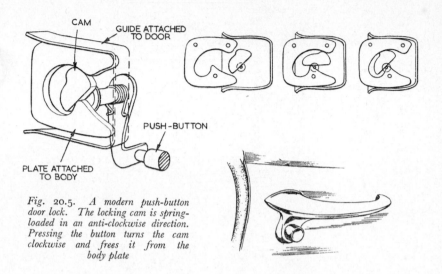

*Fig. 20.5. A modern push-button door lock. The locking cam is spring-loaded in an anti-clockwise direction. Pressing the button turns the cam clockwise and frees it from the body plate*

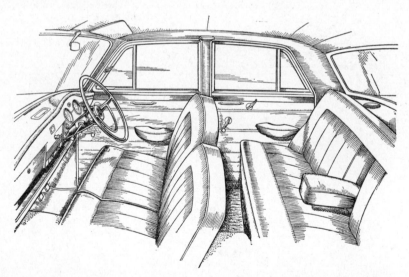

*Fig. 20.6. This car interior has split bench seating at the front; the two halves can be separately adjusted to suit two people or brought into line to accommodate three. The centre-arm at the rear can be lifted to make room for an extra rear passenger*

out completely. A bonnet catch, operated from the driver's seat, is often fitted and is a useful security against tampering.

Wind and rain are guarded against by providing moulded rubber strips, both on the doors themselves and around the door frames. Other rubber seals are provided on the windows but a certain amount of water inevitably penetrates to the door cavity. To prevent corrosion and the accumulation of water, the doors are drained and ventilated by holes in the lower edges. Rain from the roof is prevented from dripping

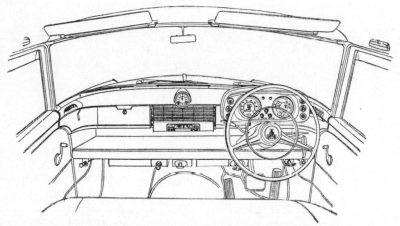

*Fig. 20.7. The driver of this car has good visibility through a wide curved windscreen. The parcel shelf extends the full width*

into an open or faulty door by means of metal gutters running along both sides of the roof and usually extending down the roof pillars.

A particularly desirable feature that has all but disappeared from the popular ranges of cars is the sunshine roof. Although a roof of this type has to be carefully designed and maintained to prevent the entry of rain, it adds greatly to the pleasure of motoring for about six months of the year. Even in moderately cool weather, a sunshine roof can be used to give light and air with very little draught. On the internally sliding type, rain is led away through channels in the roof pillars and these must be cleaned from time to time to prevent blockage. On another type, the sliding cover moves over instead of under the main body roof. Several continental cars have sunshine roofs made of fabric.

### Seating and Decoration

Front seats can be roughly divided into " bucket " and " bench " types. The bucket provides a snug seat for the driver and a similar

233

seat for his front passenger. The seat is moulded to the shape of the back and is particularly suitable for fast driving because of the side support it gives when cornering. The bench type is designed to accommodate an extra passenger at the front; with steering-column gear change and the generous width of several modern cars, three people can be seated in comfort. A compromise arrangement is the split bench type of seating; the two front seats are separately adjustable to suit the driver and rear passengers but can be brought into line to accommodate a second front passenger. Forward position adjustment is obtained by sliding the front seats on rails. The seat structure may be of sheet metal or of tubular steel.

The rear-seat structure is usually part of the bodywork and only the upholstery is detachable. On small cars the width of the rear seats is limited by the presence of the wheel arches but, with a longer wheel-base, the rear seat can extend to the full interior width of the car (Fig. 20.6).

Spring and padded upholstery has been largely superseded by the foam rubber or " Dunlopillo " type, both for the seats themselves and for back-rests. Leather is still widely employed for upholstery but on the lower-priced cars it now has to compete with plastic materials. Sometimes leather is used for hard-wearing surfaces whilst a leather substitute is used elsewhere.

Plastic materials are also being used increasingly for roof linings in place of cloth. These materials have the advantage of being washable but have a certain coldness compared with a cloth lining.

Both rubber matting and carpeting are used as flooring materials. The first is easier to keep clean while the second has a more sumptuous appearance.

Colour plays an important part in interior decorations and both manufacturers and motorists have become more colour-conscious since the war. All popular makes are supplied in a wide range of interior and exterior colour combinations of varying sobriety to suit most tastes.

Accommodation for small parcels, maps and the like is sometimes provided on a wide shelf beneath the front fascia and sometimes in glove boxes alongside the instrument panel. Whilst the latter are tidier, a shelf usually provides more room (Fig. 20.7). Other storage space may be provided beneath the seats and in door pockets and also on the ledge beneath the rear window.

# Chapter 21

---

# THE ELECTRICAL SYSTEM

THE modern car carries a formidable assortment of electrical equipment, including not only essential items such as head lamps, side lights and tail lamps, but frequently such additional equipment as a heater fan, radio, electric windscreen wipers and so on. The electrical system, dealt with in the present chaper, is therefore a very vital part of the car.

The battery and dynamo are jointly responsible for meeting all these power requirements. Whilst the dynamo alone would be able to maintain the supply during normal running, the battery is essential as a power reservoir during starting and for operating the lights and other equipment when the engine is stationary or running slowly. The present chapter deals with the major components including the battery and dynamo system, the electric starter, and also the lighting and wiring systems. The use of A.C. for power generation is also discussed.

### The Battery

Most motor-car batteries are based on the following principle. If we place two rods, one of pure lead and one of lead peroxide, in a solution of dilute sulphuric acid, an electric pressure or voltage is generated between the two rods. If, therefore, the rods are connected to a pocket lamp bulb, a current will flow and the bulb will light up (Fig. 21.1). Basically, a battery consists of a number of " cells " such as this connected together in series. The voltage generated by a single cell is about 2 volts, so that a 12 volt battery is formed by joining six cells together. In practice, plates rather than rods are used, so as to provide a larger surface area and so increase the current that can be drawn from the battery. The lead peroxide is brownish in colour and forms the positive plate while the lead plate is grey and forms the negative.

As current flows from the battery, chemical reactions take place between the acid and the two plates simultaneously. Both the lead peroxide and the lead are converted to lead sulphate, and, at the same time, water is formed. When the plates become covered in sulphate, the battery is fully discharged and requires recharging. The formation of water during discharge causes the acid solution to become weaker. As acid is heavier than water, the state of charge can easily be found by measuring the heaviness or " specific gravity " of the solution. This is done by drawing off some of the acid into a hydrometer which is simply a glass tube containing a float. If the

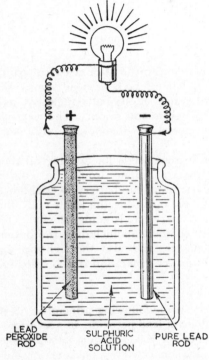

Fig. 21.1. *A simple 2-volt cell. As the cell discharges, the rods interact chemically with the acid. The acid becomes weaker and sulphate is formed on the plates*

LEAD
PEROXIDE
ROD

SULPHURIC
ACID
SOLUTION

PURE LEAD
ROD

battery is fully charged, the solution is heavy and lifts the top of the float well above the surface, whereas if the battery is flat, the float sinks to a low level. Sometimes the floats are marked with words such as " full " or " dead " and sometimes with actual numbers denoting specific gravity. A value of 1·25, for example, means that the solution is 1·25 times as heavy as pure water. The reading is about 1·28 when the battery is fully charged and falls to around 1·15 when the battery is discharged to the safe limit. Further discharge is harmful to the plates.

A battery is recharged by passing a current through it in the reverse direction. The current is drawn automatically from the dynamo during normal running and it is not usually necessary to remove the battery for charging, provided the battery is in good condition and the car is in continuous use.

The chemical changes during charging are the reverse of those that occur during discharge. Lead peroxide is re-formed at the positive plate, and pure lead at the negative plate. Water in the battery takes part in the reaction and sulphuric acid is produced. Thus the plates return to their original condition and the strength of the acid solution is restored. If charging is continued after the battery has become fully charged, there is no lead sulphate on the plates for the oxygen and hydrogen to combine with, and bubbling or " gassing " occurs. The only attention normally required by the battery is the occasional addition of distilled water to the individual cells, to replace the water lost by gassing and evaporation. No acid is lost by the battery in normal use except by evaporation and this loss is so small as to be negligible. Unless acid has been spilled, it should not be necessary to add acid to the battery.

The battery requires very careful design to ensure long life and good load capacity. High capacity is obtained by sandwiching a number of

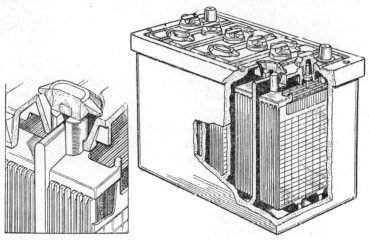

*Fig. 21.2. A 12-volt battery is made up from six 2-volt cells. Each cell contains inter-leaved gangs of plates so as to increase the surface area and hence the amp-hour capacity and the permissible discharge current*

positive and negative plates together in each cell (Fig. 21.2). Non-conducting separators made of porous rubber, wood or other material are used to keep the plates apart and prevent a short circuit inside the battery. Each gang of positive or negative plates is joined together at the top, and the positive and negative gangs of adjacent cells are linked together. Each plate consists of a lead grid either packed with a spongy form of lead or coated with a paste of lead peroxide. This form of design enables the chemical reactions to take place over a wide surface and in a small space.

The capacity of a battery is measured in amp-hours and is found by multiplying the number of amps by the number of hours for which the current flows. Thus a battery of 50 amp-hours capacity should deliver a current of 5 amps for 10 hours. The capacity depends to

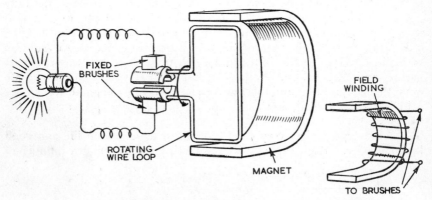

*Fig. 21.3. Principle of the dynamo. Voltage is only generated whilst the loop is passing the ends of the magnet. The flow of current from a single-loop dynamo is therefore intermittent. In practice, the permanent magnet is replaced by an electro-magnet, fed with current from the brushes (inset)*

some extent on the rate of discharge and tends to be higher if the discharge rate is low. Thus the same battery might deliver 3 amps for 20 hours and its capacity would then be 60 amp-hours.

### The Dynamo

The function of the dynamo is to supply the current required for recharging the battery and so avoid the necessity for connecting the battery to an external charger at frequent intervals. The dynamo is usually mounted on the side of the engine and driven by a V belt from the crankshaft as shown in Fig. 3.1.

The principle of the dynamo can be briefly explained in the following way. If a loop of wire is rotated between the ends of a horseshoe magnet, an electric pressure or voltage is generated between the ends of the loop (Fig. 21.3). The electricity can be picked up by stationary carbon " brushes " bearing against copper pieces attached to the ends of the loop and can be used for lighting or other purposes.

A magnetic field can also be produced by passing a current through a coil of wire (as mentioned in connection with ignition on p. 67). We can therefore replace the permanent magnet by a piece of soft iron of similar shape and magnetize it by passing a current through a " field " winding (Fig. 21.3 inset). An electromagnet makes it possible to regulate the output voltage by varying the field current as discussed below. The field current is drawn from the dynamo itself by connecting the field terminals to the brushes.

The voltage is only generated as the wires move past the ends of the magnet and the current can only flow while the loop ends are in contact with the brushes. Consequently the supply is intermittent and in an actual dynamo it is necessary to have a number of loops spaced at regular intervals. The loop ends are spaced round a cylindrical " commutator " and the brushes make contact with whichever loop is passing under the ends of the magnet (Fig. 21.4).

## Voltage Control

The voltage generated by a dynamo is normally low when the speed is low and rises as the speed increases. It is necessary on a motor car

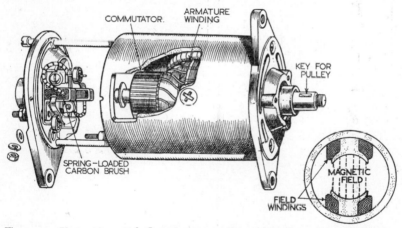

*Fig. 21.4. To provide a steady flow of current, a dynamo must use a number of loops, each having its ends connected to a pair of segments, one on each side of the commutator. In practice, each loop has a considerable number of turns in order to increase the generated voltage*

to provide some method of voltage control so that the dynamo generates sufficient voltage to charge the battery even when the engine speed is moderately low. At the same time, the voltage must not be allowed to rise excessively at high speed, otherwise the battery may be damaged by overcharging and the lights may be burnt out.

On modern cars, the dynamo voltage is controlled by continuous regulation of the field current. A resistance is placed in the field circuit and is initially short-circuited by a switch to ensure high field current and hence high output voltage when the dynamo speed is low (Fig. 21.5). When the dynamo voltage exceeds a certain value, an electromagnet, fed by the dynamo, causes the switch to open and the field current and output voltage immediately fall. The voltage across the electromagnet also falls causing the switch to close once more. This cycle of operations repeats itself rapidly and the dynamo voltage is maintained reasonably constant at the pre-set value.

If the battery is at all flat, the battery voltage will be considerably lower than the dynamo voltage and the charging current will be high. As the battery voltage builds up, it resists the flow of the charging current which therefore falls, thus preventing overcharging.

In addition to the main winding, the electromagnet may carry a " series " winding through which the charging current flows. If the

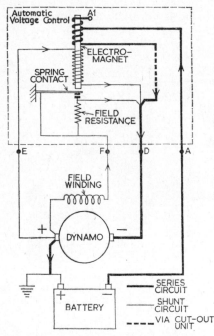

Fig. 21.5. *Automatic voltage control. The dynamo voltage is regulated by controlling the field current. If the voltage rises too high, the electromagnet opens the contacts and the field current is reduced. The top coil on the magnet produces the same effect when the charging current to the battery becomes excessive. The letters correspond to those used for identifying these terminals on many modern cars*

charging current is excessive, the contacts open and the field current is reduced. Usually, much of the car's electrical equipment is connected between earth and the terminal shown as A1 in Fig. 21.5. Consequently, as the load current increases, the dynamo voltage falls, so tending to reduce the current supplied to the load. A further refinement is a temperature-sensitive device which tends to keep the contacts closed when the unit is cold, thus providing a charging boost for a short period after starting.

## Automatic Cut-out

If the dynamo were directly connected to the battery, a serious difficulty would arise. When the car was out of use or when the dynamo speed was very low, the battery would discharge through the dynamo and tend

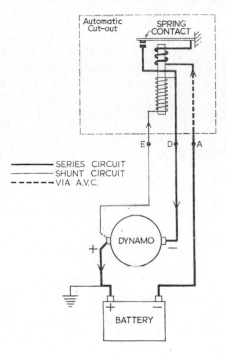

*Fig. 21.6. Automatic cut-out. When the dynamo voltage is low, the contacts are open and the battery cannot discharge through the dynamo. The contacts are closed by the current in the shunt coil when the dynamo voltage rises; the charging current can then flow through the closed circuit. Should the battery discharge, the series coil opposes the pull of the shunt coil and the contacts open*

to drive it as an electric motor. The drain on the battery would be exceedingly heavy since the dynamo is mechanically coupled to the engine. To avoid this trouble an automatically operated switch or cut-out is placed in one of the leads between the battery and the dynamo (Fig. 21.6).

The construction of the cut-out is similar to that of the automatic voltage control. The cut-out contacts are made to close by the magnetic pull of a solenoid or electromagnet which is fed with the dynamo voltage through a " shunt " winding. The action of a spring causes the contacts to remain open until the dynamo voltage has risen to a fairly high value. The solenoid also carries a " series " winding through which the current between the dynamo and the battery passes. When the dynamo is charging, the magnetic pull of this winding helps to keep the contacts closed. If, however, the dynamo voltage falls below that of the battery, the direction of the current is reversed so that the series winding opposes the shunt winding. The contacts immediately open, thus preventing discharge of the battery.

The voltage-control and cut-out systems are usually mounted in a single group which may also serve as a junction and fuse box and can contain spare fuses.

### The Starter

To turn over a cold engine fast enough to get good compression in the cylinders and make the engine fire, requires a considerable turning

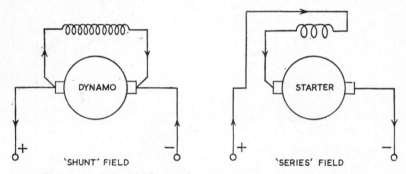

'SHUNT' FIELD     'SERIES' FIELD

Fig. 21.7. *A shunt field is used for the dynamo so as to make the generated voltage independent of the load current. A series field is used for the starter in order to obtain high torque during starting when the current is high*

effort, whether the engine be started by hand or by means of the electric starter motor. As the available voltage is only 12 volts, the electric starter has to draw a current of several hundred amperes from the battery in order to develop the required power. Fortunately, the current drops rapidly as soon as the engine starts to turn and the starter is only required to operate for a second or two. It would be impossible to pass so heavy a current through so small a motor continuously without overheating.

The basic construction of the starter motor is similar in principle to that of the dynamo which was outlined in Fig. 21.3. Instead of the armature, that is the windings, being *turned* and current being drawn *from* the commutator brushes, current is supplied *to* the brushes and the armature *develops* power. The current supplied to the brushes flows through the armature which then behaves as a magnet and is attracted by the stationary field magnet. The main difference in construction between the motor and dynamo, apart from the heavier windings required

242

by the motor for carrying the heavy starting current, is in the arrangement of the field windings. Whereas the dynamo has a " shunt " field winding connected across the brushes parallel with the armature windings, the starter field is connected in series with the armature so that the main current has to flow through the field windings (Fig. 21.7). The advantage of this arrangement is that the heavy starting current produces a correspondingly strong magnetic field and hence a high starting torque.

The mechanical drive from the starter motor to the engine is transmitted by a small cog or pinion which engages with gear teeth on the rim of the flywheel (Fig. 21.8). The starter pinion is free to move along the starter shaft and is normally held out of engagement by a

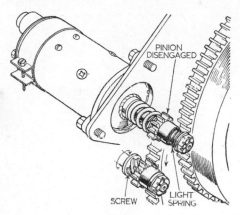

PINION
DISENGAGED

SCREW

LIGHT
SPRING

Fig. 21.8. (Left) The inertia of the starter pinion causes it to be screwed along the starter shaft towards the flywheel as the starter motor accelerates. It is flung out of mesh as soon as the engine fires

Fig. 21.9. (Right) Heavy wiring must be used for the starter circuit in order to cope with the heavy starting current without over-heating of the wiring

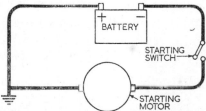

BATTERY

STARTING
SWITCH

STARTING
MOTOR

light spring. An elongated screw thread is cut inside the pinion and this mates with a corresponding thread on a sleeve which is driven by the starter shaft. When the shaft begins to turn, the pinion lags behind and therefore moves along the sleeve into mesh with the flywheel. The sleeve on which the starter pinion rides is driven through a heavy spring which relieves the motor of some of the shock of engagement. So long as the engine is acting as a drag on the motor, the pinion is " screwed " in this position, but as soon as the engine fires, the flywheel gives the pinion a backward kick which knocks it out of engagement. On many starters, the parts are so arranged that the starter pinion slides towards the motor during engagement.

Owing to the high starting current, the starter wiring has to be very heavy and is quite separate from the general wiring (Fig. 21.9). The length of wiring is kept to a minimum and the switch is remotely operated either by a cable connected to the starter knob on the panel or by an electromagnet.

### Lighting

The most important and controversial aspect of motor-car lighting is the design and use of the head lamps.   Not only have the lamps to provide

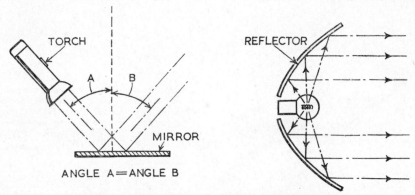

*Fig. 21.10.  Head-lamp reflectors are made " parabolic "*
*in shape so as to reflect the light in a parallel beam*

a powerful main beam for fast night driving on unlit roads; they must also incorporate a non-dazzling beam suitable for use when other traffic is approaching.

The lamps used in motor cars, like the majority of those in domestic use, produce light from the passage of an electric current through a filament made of tungsten.   The efficiency of a lamp, that is, the amount of light produced for a given power consumption, increases rapidly with the temperature at which the filament is made to operate—hence the use of tungsten which has a very high melting point and can operate at temperatures in the region of 4,000°F.

All head lamps include a highly polished reflector which collects light from the filament and throws it forward in a beam.   The design of a reflector depends on the fundamental optical principle that a ray of light is always reflected from a mirror surface at the same angle as that at which it impinges (Fig. 21.10).   The " parabolic " reflector used universally is shaped so that wherever the rays strike it they are thrown forward in a parallel beam.   Perfect beams of this sort, however, would

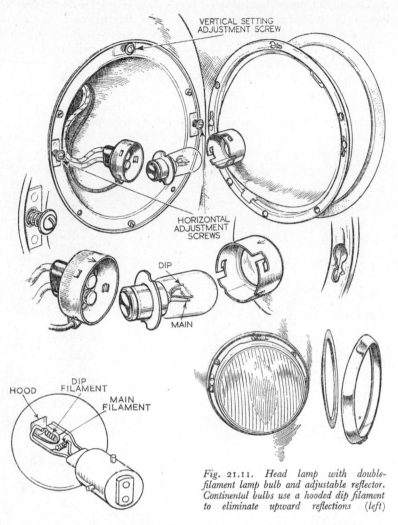

VERTICAL SETTING
ADJUSTMENT SCREW

HORIZONTAL
ADJUSTMENT
SCREWS

DIP

MAIN

HOOD

DIP
FILAMENT

MAIN
FILAMENT

*Fig. 21.11. Head lamp with double-filament lamp bulb and adjustable reflector. Continental bulbs use a hooded dip filament to eliminate upward reflections (left)*

not be satisfactory since a certain amount of spread is necessary, partly to give adequate sideways and downwards illumination at close range and partly to give a reasonably wide area of distant illumination. The use of a horizontal lamp filament causes the beam to spread sideways and further beam control is provided by the glass lamp cover. This cover is in fact broken up into lenses and prisms which deal with different parts of the beam in different ways. Light near the centre is not affected much but the upper and lower parts of the glass throw the light down-wards. The glass also assists the sideways divergence of the beam.

In the modern British and American dipping system, both head-lamp bulbs have two horizontal filaments. The main filament is placed centrally in the reflector with the second filament located above it and, in keep-left countries, offset to the right-hand side. The two filaments are separately wired and when the driver presses the dipper switch, one filament goes out and the other comes on. The location of the second filament causes the beam to be directed downwards and to the left, so eliminating the dazzle for oncoming traffic. Adjusting screws are provided in the head-lamp mounting so that the beams can be set to their correct angles (Fig. 21.11). On continental head-lamp bulbs, a

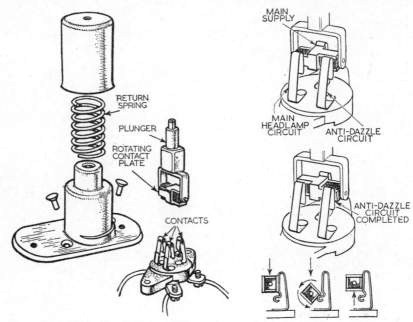

Fig. 21.12. *Foot-operated dipper switch. Each operation of the switch causes the contact plate to rotate through one quarter of a turn, so changing from one beam circuit to the other*

screen is placed under the dip filament so that light shining down on to the reflector cannot be reflected upwards. The construction of a foot-operated dipper switch is shown in Fig. 21.12.

In America, "sealed beam" head lamps are widely used. These are lamps in which the reflector, front glass and lamp filament are combined to form a single hermetically sealed unit. Accurate location of the filaments with respect to the reflector is ensured and the reflector remains perfectly clean throughout its life, but the unit is naturally more costly to replace than a plain lamp bulb.

Side lamps are occasionally incorporated in the head lamps, but are usually mounted independently below them. Alternatively they may be mounted on top of the wings and in this position the driver is able to see whether both are alight.

Beside side lamps, the car must be fitted with two red rear lamps and illumination for the rear number plate. The rear lamps are usually fitted

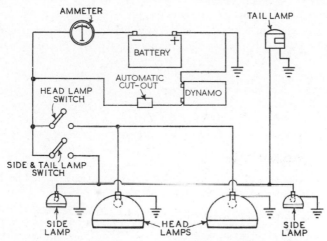

*Fig.* 21.13. *Single-pole wiring system (simplified). The return path for the current from each component is through " earth "*

with twin filaments, one for normal night use and the other for use as a brake warning light by night and by day. The switch for operating the warning lights may be mechanically operated by the brake pedal or it may be incorporated in the hydraulic system and operated by hydraulic pressure (*see* Fig. 16.8). In either case, it functions automatically when the brake pedal is depressed.

Panel lights and interior lights are provided on all modern saloon cars; often the saloon light is automatically operated by a switch in the door hinge as soon as the door is opened. Lights in the luggage boot and engine compartment and an electric socket for a portable lead lamp are less commonly provided than one might wish.

### The Wiring System

Every electrical component on a car requires a path along which current can flow from the battery and one along which it can return. One method of wiring is the " double-pole " system in which a pair of wires is led to every component. Modern practice, however, favours the "earth return" system in which the current is led to the lamp or other load through a wire and allowed to return through the body or "earth". Although the earth return system results in some simplification, the wiring remains fairly complex and a coloured cable system is used to assist in identification. A simplified wiring diagram, showing the principle of the earth return system, is given in Fig. 21.13.

Nowadays the *positive* side of the battery is usually earthed, instead of the negative, as this practice has been found to yield certain advantages. The sparking plugs can operate effectively with lower voltages and wear of the central electrode is less. Moreover, corrosion at electrical contacts and particularly at the battery terminals is reduced.

### A.C. or D.C.?

Most motor cars have direct current (D.C.) electrical systems, that is the current always flows from the dynamo in the same direction. The D.C. system used to be widely used for domestic electricity, but today most British homes are supplied with alternating current (A.C.), that is the current flows alternately in opposite directions. It now seems likely that A.C. generators will be increasingly used for motor cars.

The weakest part of a D.C. dynamo is the commutator which is the part of the rotor where the brushes pick up the current from the loops as they rotate in the magnetic field (see p. 238). The biggest advantage of A.C. is that the generator requires no commutator. The ends of the rotating loops can be taken to "slip-rings" mounted side by side on the shaft. Alternatively, the loops can be stationary while an electro-magnet rotates inside them, the magnet being fed with a small D.C. supply from the battery, again through slip-rings. Slip-rings are stronger than a commutator and there is no interruption of current to give rise to sparking. Consequently, an alternator can have a high idling speed without fear of trouble at maxium speed. Thus an alternator can charge the battery even when the engine is idling. A.C. has the disadvantage that rectifiers are needed to convert the charging current to D.C. But an automatic cut-out is no longer required since the rectifiers will not permit current to flow from the battery to the alternator.

Chapter 22

# EQUIPMENT AND ACCESSORIES

MOST modern cars carry a wide range of equipment and accessories such as petrol gauges, trafficators, wing mirrors, radios and so on. Some items are both legally and practically essential, while others are no more than gadgets and in between there is a class of things which are useful but not exactly essential. The present chapter deals with many of the items from all three classes.

### Is It Necessary?

Whether or not a piece of equipment is regarded as necessary depends very much on the point of view of the individual driver. Those who have driven 50,000 miles without a puncture but have been stranded a few times through running out of petrol, might regard a reserve petrol tank as more essential than a spare wheel. One man, who frequently drives long distances alone, may regard a radio as absolutely essential; a thriftier man, who drives in the same way, may regard a radio as desirable but not essential; while a third may regard a radio as a positive nuisance and a source of distraction and danger.

Another factor entering into the question is the mechanical aptitude of the driver. A mechanical enthusiast will probably regard an oil-pressure gauge as a necessity so that he can take proper care of his engine and receive an early warning of any lubrication trouble. A less knowledgeable driver may be needlessly worried by the normal fluctuations of such a gauge whilst a third may ignore it completely

The classification given in Table 6 could reasonably apply to a driver of average means who drives a Saloon car all the year round on British roads and who takes an interest in the mechanical state of the car.

The remainder of the chapter will be devoted to a short discussion of some of the items listed in Table 6.

### Mirrors

Every car requires a good rear mirror and every driver should cultivate the habit of glancing into it frequently. A wide rectangular

9

mirror placed centrally just behind the windscreen is the most satisfactory. The mirror can be mounted just above or just below eye level and may be flat or convex. The mirror must give a wide field of view in order to take full advantage of modern wide rear windows.

For the interior mirror, one of the wide, flat type is satisfactory but wing mirrors should preferably be convex. A convex mirror gives a

### Table 6   Classification of Accessories

#### CLASS 1: ESSENTIAL

| | |
|---|---|
| One good mirror | Petrol gauge |
| Windscreen wipers | Oil-pressure indicator |
| Direction indicators | Dynamo charging indicator |
| Horn | Water thermometer |
| Speedometer | Tools |
| Mileometer | Instruction manual |
| Heater and demister | Spare bulbs, fuses, plugs |
| Interior sun visor | Windscreen water spray |

#### CLASS 2: DESIRABLE BUT OPTIONAL

| | |
|---|---|
| Wing mirrors | Radio |
| Spare wheel | Reversing light |
| Reserve fuel tank | Parking light |
| Engine rev-counter | Extra driving lights |
| Trip mileometer | Radiator blind or muff |
| Electric clock | Oil-level indicator |

#### CLASS 3: AVAILABLE BUT UNNECESSARY

| | |
|---|---|
| Fly " deflectors " | Exhaust pipe attachments |
| Petrol " economy " devices | Venetian blinds |
| Power " boosters " | External sun visor |
| Air conditioning | Cocktail cabinets, etc. |

wider field of view than a flat or plain mirror of equal size. The distance of objects is distorted but the driver soon learns to make allowance for this automatically. With wide, rear windows, wing mirrors are perhaps less helpful than formerly, but they are still a great help, particularly for observing the traffic before pulling out to the right, for pulling in after overtaking and for extra safety in the jungle of city traffic.

### Windscreen Wipers and Sprayers

Windscreen wipers can be driven either by an electric motor or by an air motor connected to the engine induction system (Fig. 22.1). In

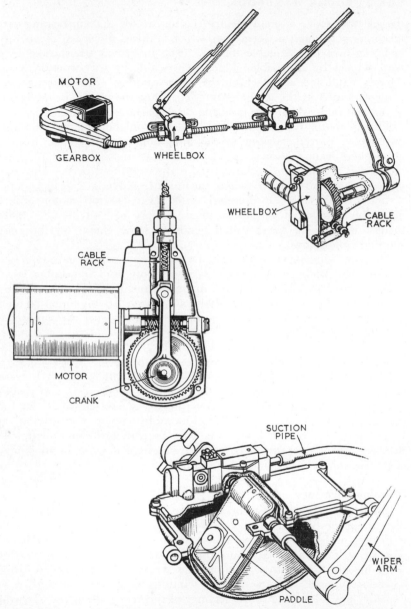

MOTOR

GEARBOX

WHEELBOX

WHEELBOX

CABLE
RACK

CABLE
RACK

MOTOR

CRANK

SUCTION
PIPE

WIPER
ARM

PADDLE

Fig. 22.1. *Windscreen wipers can be operated either by an electric motor or by an air motor connected to the engine inlet manifold. The electric type shown here operates twin wipers through a cable rack-and-pinion mechanism. The air motor is shown operating a single wiper directly. Each side of the paddle is exposed in turn to vacuum and to atmosphere*

251

the electric type, a small electric motor drives a reciprocating crank mechanism through a worm gear which reduces the speed of operation and increases the available torque. The motion is transmitted to the twin wipers by a flexible cable. The cable is wire-wound to form "teeth" and acts as a rack on the wiper pinions. Sometimes a switch is incorporated in the motor gear box so that the circuit is only broken at the end of a sweep, thus ensuring "self-parking" of the wipers.

The air-motor type depends for its action on the fact that the engine produces a partial vacuum in the induction manifold. Air from the atmosphere can therefore be made to flow through a small paddle motor and produce the work required to operate the wipers. The engine vacuum is much reduced when the throttle valve is wide open and a "vacuum reservoir" is therefore fitted between the motor and the induction manifold to ensure a steady supply of "vacuum". Nevertheless, the wiping speed still depends to some extent on the engine running conditions.

The two wipers can either be arranged to operate in phase or in opposition. If the wipers move in opposition, it is impossible for the wiped areas to overlap, and an unwiped area is left in the middle of the screen. The rubber wiper blades are always flexibly mounted on the swinging wiper arms to ensure complete contact with the windscreen, in spite of curvature.

Windscreen wipers can be completely effective only when the windscreen is thoroughly wet. Sometimes, however, in slow fine rain or when following another car on wet roads after rain has ceased, operation of the wipers results in smears on the windscreen, and visibility is worse than it was before, at any rate for a few seconds. On these occasions, a water sprayer is of considerable help to safe driving, and water sprayers are fitted to some cars as standard equipment. The sprayers can be operated electrically, by manual force or by making use of the suction in the engine inlet manifold.

### Direction Indicators

Efficient direction indicators are another aid to safe driving, when they are properly used. It has been very reasonably argued that direction indicators and brake warning lights can give quite as clear an indication of a driver's intention as any hand signal, and without any need for removing the hands from the steering wheel. Moreover, few drivers nowadays care to drive with their windows wide open in cold or wet weather, to say nothing of the feelings of the rear passengers. It would be wiser to teach the learner his duty of seeing that his rear brake warning lights and direction indicators are functioning correctly than to encourage him to worry about giving hand signals when braking in a

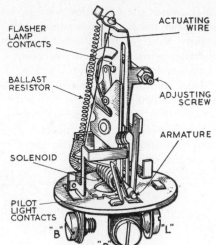

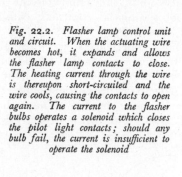

Fig. 22.2. *Flasher lamp control unit and circuit. When the actuating wire becomes hot, it expands and allows the flasher lamp contacts to close. The heating current through the wire is thereupon short-circuited and the wire cools, causing the contacts to open again. The current to the flasher bulbs operates a solenoid which closes the pilot light contacts; should any bulb fail, the current is insufficient to operate the solenoid*

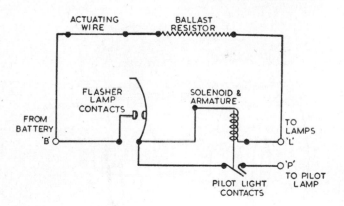

hurry.   Unfortunately, if he heeded this advice, he would probably fail his test.

The " semaphore " or " trafficator " arm type of indicator has been largely superseded by " flasher " indicators.   In the semaphore type, an electromagnet exerts a pull on a plunger when the driver operates the indicator switch, causing the arm to swing out.   The flasher type uses a special type of thermal expansion switch (Fig. 22.2).   When the indicators are not being used, the flasher-lamp contacts are prevented from closing by the tension in the actuating wire.   When the trafficator switch is operated in either direction, a low current is passed through the actuating wire.   The current is insufficient to light the flasher bulbs,

253

but it causes the actuating wire to become hot and to expand. When the flasher-lamp contacts close, they not only allow sufficient current to flow to light the flasher-lamp bulbs, but they short-circuit the actuating wire. The wire becomes cool again and contracts, causing the flasher-lamp contacts to open again.

Many motorists, including the author, experienced an instinctive feeling of dislike for the flasher indicator when it was first introduced, but now that the system is established, several of its advantages ought to be admitted. The door pillars no longer have to accommodate the semaphore indicators and can therefore be more slender. The flashers are clearly visible from front and rear. Also the flasher system is cheap

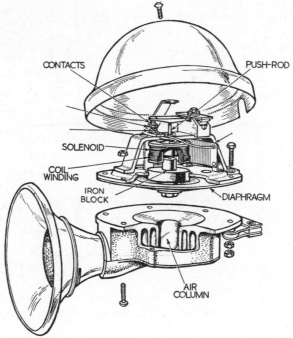

Fig. 22.3. *Electric wind-tone horn. The solenoid attracts the iron block attached to the diaphragm and causes the diaphragm to vibrate*

and easy to maintain. When the flasher system is used, it is important that an interior pilot light should be fitted to operate only when the flashers are working correctly.

One of the disadvantages of the system is the difficulty of obtaining satisfactory brightness. Flashers which are clearly visible by day can be irritatingly bright at night. There is a strong case for fitting a resistance in the circuit which can be switched into use at night if required. A further objection is the lack of uniformity in colour and the fact that faulty rear flashers and rear brake warning lights can be very confusing.

## The Horn

The horn is essentially a means of attracting the attention of other road users when it is likely that they may not be making proper allowance for one's presence. Although the horn should never be relied upon as a

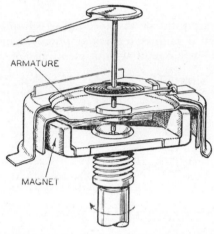

ARMATURE

MAGNET

*Fig. 22.4. A magnetically operated speedometer. The magnet is driven from the transmission side of the gear box and induces eddy currents in the armature to which the pointer is attached. The armature becomes magnetized and is dragged through an angle which increases with the speed of the magnet*

means of averting danger, from time to time its use makes an important contribution to road safety. When one is tempted to use the horn to express anger, frustration, impatience or mere slap-happiness, one should remember that unnecessary use detracts from the importance of the horn as a warning device. The sound from a modern electric horn, like the note of a bugle, is produced by the vibration of a column of air in a resonator tube. The air column is set in motion by a diaphragm which is vibrated by means of an electromagnet (Fig. 22.3). In principle, the vibrator operates in the same way as an electric bell. When the button is pressed, an electric current is made to pass through a coil of wire or solenoid which thereupon acts like a magnet and attracts a small iron block towards it. In an electric bell the block is attached to the bell striker, while in an electric horn it is attached to the diaphragm. The motion of the block is also imparted to a pushrod which causes a

255

pair of electric contacts to open, thus interrupting the supply to the electromagnet. The block then returns to its original position causing the contacts to close again and the whole sequence repeats itself so long as the horn button is despressed.

The pitch of the horn depends on the size of the resonator tube and the frequency of vibration of the vibrator. As both of these are fixed by the design, the pitch of a horn cannot be adjusted. Many cars are fitted with a pair of horns each with its own note.

### Instruments

It is not always easy to judge the speed at which one is driving and a reliable speedometer is both a legal and practical necessity. On the usual type, the pointer is mounted on a metal disc or armature in front

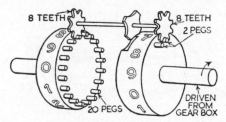

*Fig. 22.5. Principle of the mileometer. The wheel on the left, recording tens of miles, rotates by one tenth of a turn for every complete turn of the wheel on the right*

of a rotating magnet which is driven from the rear of the gear box through a flexible cable (Fig. 22.4). The motion of the magnet generates electric currents in the disc and these currents make the disc magnetic. The magnet therefore tends to drag the disc round with it and the force of attraction increases with the speed of rotation of the magnet. The movement of the disc and pointer is resisted by a weak spring and, provided the dial has been correctly calibrated, the movement of the pointer gives a reasonably correct indication of the speed of the vehicle.

An engine rev-counter is similar in construction to a speedometer but the drive is taken from the engine side of the gear box. The rev-counter is useful for judging engine speed when changing gear and for avoiding over-speeding and low-speed " slogging " of the engine. However, except when the clutch pedal is depressed, the engine speed is related to the forward speed of the car and can be deduced from the speedometer reading.

As the distance covered by a car is proportional to the number of turns of the speedometer cable, the mileometer can be incorporated in the speedometer, though it is, in principle, a separate instrument (Fig. 22.5). The first wheel of the instrument, which may record either tenths or whole miles, is driven from the cable through a reduction gear. Each time this wheel rotates through a whole turn, it causes the next wheel to rotate by one tenth of a turn and so on. Some speedometers also carry a " trip " mileometer which reads up to one thousand miles and can be quickly set back to zero. This is very useful for logging journey distances and for checking petrol consumption. The trip mileometer can be zeroed when the tank is nearly empty, and its reading noted when the tank is again nearly empty after using 10, 20 or 30 gallons depending on the accuracy required.

The following instruments have already been referred to on the pages indicated: petrol gauge (p. 81), oil pressure gauge (p. 95), water thermometer (p. 111), dynamo charging indicator (p. 73).

An oil-level indicator is an instrument that gives a panel reading of the level of oil in the engine sump and thereby eliminates the necessity for frequent examination of the dipstick. It works in the same way as a petrol gauge.

### The Heater and Demister

An effective heater converts a long journey in winter from an ordeal into a pleasure and is coming to be regarded as an essential part of the modern car. The majority of car heaters heat the air inside the car by blowing it over metal surfaces which are heated by the engine cooling water (see Fig. 9.7). To obtain an adequate supply of hot air it is necessary to use an electric fan and a special heat exchanger containing a large area of heating surface. In the " fresh-air " type of heater the fan draws its air from outside the car, often through a special intake in the bonnet, to avoid drawing in the engine fumes. If the intake is well located, the wind pressure due to the speed of the car is sufficient for the fan to be superfluous under many conditions. The " recirculation " type of heater draws warm air from the saloon itself and delivers it back at a higher temperature. The fresh-air type has to heat the air from a low temperature and is therefore larger and more expensive. The recirculation type, however, is less healthy and tends to cause misting of the windows.

The heater can also be made to serve as a demister by ducting some of the air to the base of the windscreen. This feature prevents " steaming up " in cold, humid weather and is also useful for keeping a clear windscreen despite frost, ice and snow. In severe conditions, such as these, the whole supply of hot air can be diverted to the demister ducts.

### Temperature Control

The capacity of the engine cooling system has to be sufficient to prevent overheating on long, steep hills on a hot day, with the result that the engine is usually over-cooled in normal winter running. Over-cooling does not necessarily harm an engine but it results in thicker oil and higher friction losses. Also, petrol may adhere to the manifold and cylinder walls and fail to become vaporized. Both these effects tend to reduce the available power and increase the petrol consumption.

Most modern cars are fitted with thermostats for controlling the engine operating temperature (*see* p. 110). The thermostat causes the cooling water to by-pass the radiator when the engine temperature is below a certain value. This greatly reduces the time required for the engine to warm up but leads to a certain difficulty in cold weather. Whilst the thermostat is closed, the water in the radiator is out of circulation and becomes cold, so that when the thermostat opens, this colder water is pumped round the engine. Consequently, the engine temperature fluctuates and this may prevent the engine giving its best performance. Moreover, the average cooling water temperature may be rather low and the heater will be less effective.

This last difficulty can be overcome by using a " winter " thermostat, that is, one that opens at a higher temperature. Another solution is the use of an exterior radiator muff which can be opened or closed to suit the weather. Alternatively, the radiator can be fitted with a blind controlled by a cable from the driver's seat. Blinds are available for most modern radiators and, if properly designed and fitted, provide easy and effective control of water temperature.

**The Radio**

There appear to be two schools of thought on the desirability of a radio. There are those who regard the radio as a distraction and danger and those who regard it as a relaxation. It would seem to the author that, provided one is capable of driving safely in the presence of passengers, one should also be capable of driving safely whilst listening to the radio, since the latter can be more readily ignored when the occasion demands. The question cannot be settled, however, without examining figures relating to the occurrence of accidents to cars with and without radios.

The main differences between a car radio and a domestic receiver, apart from size, arise from the fact that a car radio has to operate from a 12 volt battery and is subject to greater radio interference. The radio valve, which is used in amplifying the weak radio waves from the broadcasting station, normally requires a hundred volts or so, and car radios, hitherto, have included a " power pack " for stepping up the battery voltage. In recent sets, however, the power pack has been eliminated by the use of special low-voltage valves and transistors, both of which can operate at battery voltage. Transistors will perform the duties of a radio valve but are much smaller and consume less power.

### Gadgets

In using the word gadget, the author has no wish to disparage the many useful devices that have been placed on the market to meet individual needs that are not catered for by the manufacturers. There are, however, many other devices whose usefulness is so trivial or obscure that they can be called gadgets without disparaging them unduly.

A year or two ago, there was a boom in fly " deflectors ". Now a device which really would keep the windscreen clean in the summer would be extremely useful. Unfortunately, a real deflector would have to be rather large and would also have a high wind resistance and be rather unsightly. Nevertheless, the market became flooded with deflectors, whose effect was so small as to be negligible.

It is clear, therefore, that the motorist must be on his guard when examining the claims made by the less reputable accessory manufacturers. In particular, he should be very suspicious of any device which claims to give him greater power without greater petrol consumption or lower petrol consumption without loss of power. The engine and carburettor manufacturers can usually be relied upon to produce the best combination for a particular class of car. It will not usually be possible to improve the performance appreciably without some large modification, such as increasing the compression ratio or fitting twin carburettors.

# Firestone

## build tyres
## for safety and
## long mileage

**Firestone TYRES**

— consistently good

DRIVE SAFELY

**EXPERIENCE COUNTS**

45 *Factories throughout the world. Firestone total sales exceed £1,000,000 per day.*
*Firestone have made over 50,000,000 Tubeless Tyres.*

# INDEX

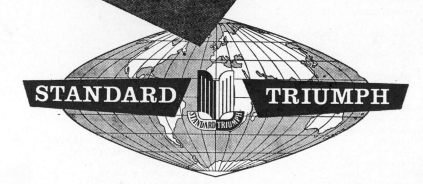

# Proven on the roads
# of the world

★★★★★ ★★★★★★★★★★★★★★★★★★★★★★★★★★★★★★★★★★★★★★★★★★★★★★★★

**STANDARD** **TRIUMPH**

**S T A N D A R D — T R I U M P H   G R O U P**
Factories : Coventry
London Showrooms: Berkeley Square, W.1.   GROsvenor 8181

267

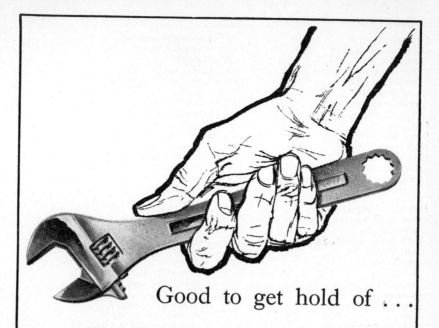

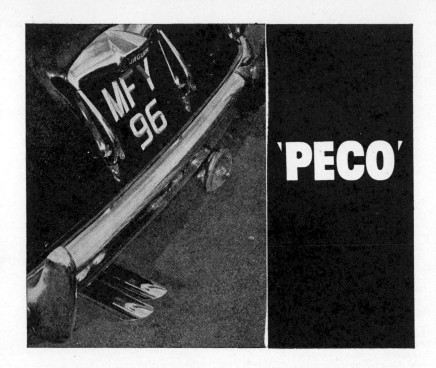

## Exhaust Engineering at its Finest

PECOPHASE "Bolt-On" Tuning Equipment is truly exhaust engineering at its finest. Extensive research and independent road tests have proved that PECOPHASE Equipment increases performance with more economy, and it is designed for every make of car.

Make sure you fit PECOPHASE Equipment, the guarantee of improved performance.

### PERFORMANCE EQUIPMENT CO. LTD.

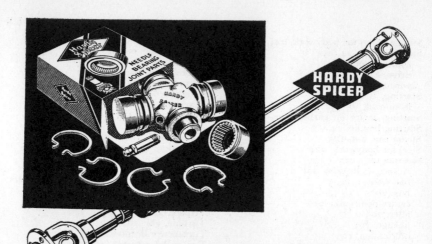

# INSIST ON
# HARDY SPICER
# REPLACEMENTS

The *Hardy Spicer reconditioned shaft scheme
covers the majority of 'popular' 1936-60 passenger cars.
In your own garage it is now possible for you to
make the replacement yourself—easily and quickly.

Make sure that genuine Hardy Spicer spares
are used when your needle
bearing joint parts need replacing.

*Applies to Great Britain only.

# HARDY SPICER

## PROPELLER SHAFTS

HARDY SPICER LTD · CHESTER RD · ERDINGTON · BIRMINGHAM 24

Automotive Division of Birfield Industries Limited

Member of the **Birfield Group**

# Save Time ▶

A BRITOOL set costs LESS than it SAVES in time. Available in ALL combinations and for ALL industries. Socket, Ring, Open jaw and many other wrenches in English, American, Unified & Metric sizes. Chrome Alloy Steel, superbly finished. Longest possible life.

THERE IS A BRITOOL SET TO SUIT YOUR REQUIREMENTS.

## TOOL UP WITH

## MANUFACTURED BY

# BRITOOL WORKS · BUSBURY
# WOLVERHAMPTON

*The*

*fire-pump engine*

*that*

*wins*

*races*

𝒞𝑜𝑣𝑒𝑛𝑡𝑟𝑦 𝒞𝑙𝑖𝑚𝑎𝑥 𝐸𝑛𝑔𝑖𝑛𝑒𝑠 𝐿𝑡𝑑.

COVENTRY, ENGLAND

BACKED BY
MORE THAN
50 YEARS
OF ENGINE
BUILDING

# STEERING GEARS

**for Private and Commercial Vehicles and Tractors**
**Power Steerings**

# OIL PUMPS

**for internal combustion engines**

# BURMAN & SONS LTD.

**Wychall Lane · Kings Norton · Birmingham 30**

# BEFORE
# YOU START . . .

go to your local Shell station. Ask for the Touring Service postcard. By return you will receive road maps of all the countries through which you will pass and other useful information. Quite free.

Be sure your car is ready too. Book an early appointment with your local Shell station for Shellubrication—the full servicing which will ensure care-free motoring.

# AND WHEREVER
# YOU GO . . .

you are never far from a Shell Service Station where you will find a friendly welcome, efficient attention and everything your car needs. Here you can obtain Shell petrols with the exclusive Ignition Control Additive, I.C.A., and Shell X-100 Motor Oil—both Multigrade and regular grades—to keep your car running smoothly throughout the journey.

There are over 1,000 Shell Touring Information Centres along the main motoring routes of Europe. Call in wherever you see the welcoming Shell Touring Service sign.

SHELL TOURING SERVICE

# YOU
# CAN BE
# SURE
# OF SHELL

279

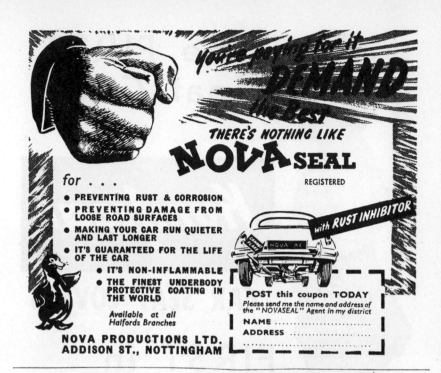

# Britain's finest motoring journal

THE AUTOCAR was founded in 1895 — Britain's and the world's first motoring journal. From that day to this it has never looked back. It maintains an uncompromising tradition of the highest standards, its contributors are consistently drawn from leading experts and engineers. Read it for first-rate accounts of technical advances; for top racing, rally, and sports reports; to get the best from your own motoring; for the practical interest of its supremely thorough road tests; or for pure enjoyment. Today there may be others in the field, but THE AUTOCAR is still alone — at the head.

FRIDAYS Is

---

## FOR YOUR FURTHER READING

### AUTOMOBILE ELECTRICAL EQUIPMENT

Theory and practice for students, designers, automobile electricians and motorists

A. P. Young, OBE, MIEE, MI MECH. E, FIWM, and L. Griffiths, MI MECH. E, AMIEE

**30s net** (by post 31s 6d)   8¾″ × 5½″   398 pp.   361 illustrations

### MECHANICS OF ROAD VEHICLES

A textbook for students, draughtsmen and automobile engineers

W. Steeds, OBE, B SC., ACGI, MI MECH. E

**35s net** (by post 36s 4d)   8¾″ × 5½″   about 300 pp.   Fully illustrated

### THE MOTOR VEHICLE

A textbook for students, draughtsmen and owner-drivers

K. Newton, MC, B SC., ACGI, AM INST. CE, MI MECH. E, and W. Steeds, OBE, B SC., ACGI, MI MECH. E

**45s net** (by post 46s 9d)   8¾″ × 5½″   684 pp.   620 illustrations

---

*From leading booksellers*

# ILIFFE & SONS LIMITED

DORSET HOUSE, STAMFORD STREET, LONDON, S.W.I

---

## INDEX TO ADVERTISERS